AGAINST THE ODDS

ISBN: 978-1-943929-16-0

Published by:
TGS International
P.O. Box 355, Berlin, Ohio 44610 USA
Phone: 330-893-4828
Fax: 330-893-2305
www.tgsinternational.com

TGS001273

AGAINST THE ODDS

RACHAEL LOFGREN

DEDICATION

Dedicated with love to Judy Yoder, my "Paul" in the fellowship of His sufferings. You have taught me the beautiful fragility of life, the meaning of suffering, and the love of Jesus in profound ways. You live Philippians 3:10 with radiance.

Forever,
Your own "Timothy"

ACKNOWLEDGMENTS

The journey of writing a book is always just that, a journey. And it is never a journey walked entirely alone. Writing a book is a little like nurturing a child. You as a parent have the most direct and significant responsibility, but those around you also play a significant role. So to all those who took part in yet another book project, thank you!

Special thanks goes to my personal editing team: Patti L., Barb Smith, and Lizzy L. Thanks for letting me count on you in so many ways through the birth of these pages! You each play such an integral role in my writing efforts. I would be lost without you!

Thank you to G. J. Hoffman for all the shared hours of writing. Brainstorming with you when I'm stuck is a perfect solution to writer's block. I love having another author as my best friend!

Thank you to Vera's family for taking me in and making their hearts and their homes such a warm place to lay the foundation for this project. Every contribution was a gift. Thank you for sharing of yourselves, your memories, and your love. I am honored to have had the opportunity to step into your happy family circus!

To Dwight Miller and C. Hostetler who envisioned this project and labored over researching and preserving Vera's legacy: this book would not exist today without your persistence and willingness to share your efforts with me in the form of written research materials and interviews. I honor your careful work and am incredibly grateful for the uncounted hours of labor you invested as forerunners and researchers of this book.

To Vera's parents and siblings, whose lives of quiet but tremendous love and sacrifice made Vera's life and testimony possible for her, your example of selflessness and servant hearts shine brightly.

And to Vera, whose love and life left a mountain-sized legacy behind her. Thank you for the example you lived and the lives you impacted while you were here with us. I never met you on earth, but I look forward to meeting you in heaven. Your legacy lives on.

And above all, thanks to God. My purpose for writing comes from you. May these pages bring you glory.

—Rachael Lofgren

CONTENTS

CHAPTER 1

STORMS AND SHADOWS

"Lena!" I exclaimed to my toddler sister, "we're birds and we're flying!" The mellow May breeze wafted through Hartville, Ohio, caressing my tousled hair as I turned in wide circles. I stretched out my arms, and my skirt twirled around my bare ankles. Lena stretched her chubby arms to imitate me and wobbled on unsteady legs. I laughed and she giggled.

"Lena, birds sing," I added after a moment. "We should sing too." I broke into a joyous warbling song composed in my three-year-old mind, making Lena giggle again. My arms swooped and my small feet danced. I almost felt as if I were actually flying!

My make-believe ended when I heard my older sister calling, "Lunch time, Vera. Grandma says to bring Lena and wash up. Hurry!" Turning to Lena, I hoisted her into our little red wagon. "Maybe we will have soup," I told her. "Grandma makes good soup."

"Hungry," Lena agreed. "Good soup." She was almost a year and a half and still couldn't talk very well, but we always understood each other. Even when we fought, we made it up to each other.

"Grandma says to hurry." I turned toward the house, puffing with the effort of pulling the wagon.

Inside we found our grandma bustling around the kitchen as usual. My five-year-old sister Ruth was dutifully helping to put on the food, and I could hear Mama's soft voice from somewhere in the house telling my brother Leon it was time for lunch. Leon was just younger than me and just older than Lena. I hurried to help Lena wash her chubby hands before sliding into my usual place on one of the long benches.

Sure enough, Grandma had made soup. I was so hungry I couldn't help peeking a bit during our silent prayer to watch the steam waft upward from my bowl. As soon as Dad said "Amen," I took a tiny sip of broth from my spoon. *Mmmm.* It was delicious! But then my ears perked up when I heard Mama say something to Dad, and my spoon hung poised in mid-air for a moment.

"I need to go into town for groceries this afternoon," Mama was saying. Putting my spoon down with a clatter, I wiggled excitedly in my seat. If Mama was going for groceries, maybe she would take me with her! I looked across the table at Lena, busily eating her soup, broth dribbling down her chin. Lena would be too young to go to town. But not me. I was a big girl. The very thought set my brown eyes dancing with delight. I just knew Mama would take me!

When Mama got ready to go that afternoon, I followed her outside. "Mama, can I come with you?" I stood eagerly on my tiptoes waiting for what I was sure would be her answer.

"Not this time, Vera. You can stay home and play with Leon and Lena. You'll have a good time." She stooped to kiss me briefly, her bonnet strings brushing the side of my face.

"But, Mama," I protested hastily. "Please? I want to come with you," I pleaded.

"No, dear. Not today." Mama was gentle but firm. "Go and play, and be good for Grandma." With that she turned and climbed into the car.

I knew then that she was in earnest. All my pleadings and entreaties would be in vain. But I had set my heart on going, and when I set my heart on something I did not give up easily. Suddenly I knew what I would do.

Slipping quietly to the front of the car, I planted myself next to the bumper. If Mama wouldn't let me go with her, then I wouldn't let her go at all. I planted my bare feet firmly and pitted my puny strength against that big metal bumper, defying it to move me. With all the determination my little mind held at that moment, I was certain it couldn't. Our Ford had always held happy memories of going away for me, but now it was my enemy.

I heard the engine rumble to life and felt it vibrate through the vehicle. I pushed harder as Mama put the car into gear and began to move forward. Then suddenly I slipped. Before I had time to cry out, half my body was under the car and the huge blackness of the tire was over me. A thump. A scream. Yelling. It was all a blur of noise and pain.

I felt Dad's strong hands lifting me and stopped screaming. "Is she okay, Victor? Oh, the blood! I didn't see her. Oh, Vera, my baby!" Mama was crying.

With a deft movement of his hand, Dad flipped the piece of my peeled scalp back into place. "There's skull showing and a whole lot of blood. It's bad, Emma, but she's alive. Open the car door for me. We need to get her to the hospital immediately."

I tasted blood on my tongue. I felt Dad place me gently but hurriedly onto the back seat of the Ford. The pain blocked most everything from my focus. "It hurts!" I was sobbing.

Then I felt gentle arms pull me close, and I knew I was in Mama's lap. Her touch comforted and calmed me. Her voice was soothing but strained. "It's okay, Vera. Mama's here. Shhh . . ." Between calming me, she prayed in whispers and pled with Dad to drive faster.

Dad's deep voice was reassuring. "Emma, we will be there soon now. It's okay." He was driving much faster than normal. I could tell by the way we slid to a stop at each intersection. The car would jerk fast and hard as he slammed on the brakes. The jerking made my pain worse, and I couldn't stop crying.

At the hospital Dad carried me inside. Somehow in his arms the pain didn't feel as bad. When he laid me on the gurney, the intensity of pain returned along with fear. What were they going to do to me? Would they put needles into me? "Vera, we're going to fix you up," the doctor calmly reassured. I lay very still and cried.

They stitched me up and sent me home with a white turban wrapped around my head. Mama held me all the way home. The twelve-inch sutured wound would form a foot-long scar on the side of my head. I wore the turban for the rest of the summer. Although the accident was traumatic enough, none of us knew that the storm that was to come three months later would overshadow it.

In the wee hours of a sultry Friday morning in August, I awoke crying. I slid out of bed in my long white nightdress and pattered across the creaking floorboards to my parents' bedroom. "Mama," I rasped urgently. Standing in their doorway, I waited for Mama to wake up, knowing she always did when I needed her.

"Yes, Vera?" She slipped out of bed and stooped down for me to come to her. "What's wrong, little one?" she asked in a whisper. Dad was still asleep.

"Mama, my head hurts."

She felt my forehead with her soft, cool hand. "Oh my, you're hot! Come, Mama will help you."

Leading me to the living room, she laid me on the sofa and went to get a cool cloth. "Here, take this." She was back with a spoon and the bottle of fever medicine we used for baby Lena when she was teething. I opened my mouth and took the liquid, making a face at its sickening sweetness and bitter after-taste. It hurt to swallow, and my throat felt thick.

"Mama, my neck hurts."

She sat down beside me and stroked my hair back from my forehead. "Shh, Vera, Mama is right here with you and you will soon be better. Just rest now." She bathed my hot face and hands and sang to me softly in German. After a while I fell into a restless sleep. I awoke to find Mama gone and early morning sunlight streaming in the window.

Dad had just come in from milking the cows. I could hear him upstairs calling the other children to get up for breakfast. If we slept too late, we would suffer the dire consequences of being pulled out of bed by our feet. One such experience usually sufficed to teach any sleepyhead to rise when our dad's booming voice called us to start the day.

I could smell coffee and hear the sizzling of bacon in the frying pan mingling with Grandma and Mama's soft voices as they made breakfast in the kitchen together. I tried to turn my head when Dad entered the living room a moment later. Crying out, I shut my eyes tight against the pain. My neck was stiff, and my head pounded. Tears formed in my eyes as my father stooped over me.

"What's wrong, Vera? Mama told me you weren't feeling so well this morning."

"My head hurts." My voice came out scarcely above a whisper. "It hurts when I move it."

"Hmm . . ." His tone was thoughtful. "Do you want something to eat?"

I shook my head slightly.

"Okay. You just rest then." He patted my shoulder gently and left the room.

The morning dragged long. After the breakfast dishes were done, Mama brought me a cool drink of water. But swallowing hurt, and I refused more than a few sips.

"Vera, you must drink something," she worried. "You have a fever. Come, try a few more sips."

I cried and refused. "Mama, hold me," I begged. She took me in her lap and rocked me. This comforted me, and I dozed and awoke by turns. Again at lunch I refused food. And when Dad came to see me before he left the house after eating, he went away looking worried. "I think I'll call Dr. Ream and see if he can come around for a visit this afternoon," I heard him tell Mama as he left.

When Dr. Ream came with the black bag he used for house calls, he took my temperature and listened to my heart and lungs. After finishing his examination, he looked grave. He left medicine with Mama "to bring the fever down," he said. His parting words were, "If her fever won't come down or she has trouble breathing, don't hesitate to take her to the hospital."

Afternoon dragged into evening and my whole body ached miserably. My head pounded. My crying had turned to feeble whimpers. I was too tired to cry in earnest.

"Mama?"

"Yes, little one?" Mama's soft eyes met mine tenderly.

"Mama, will I be better soon?"

"I pray so, Vera. Just be quiet and rest."

Evening shadows lengthened over the hills of Ohio when Dad's long strides brought him in from the barn. "Any better?" His voice was quieter than usual.

I saw Mama shake her head and I could see the worry in her eyes. Her voice was equally quiet. "I'm afraid she's worse, Vic. Her limbs are stiff. "

"How is her fever?" He came over, looking down at me with earnest concern. Mama pressed her hand to my forehead. "Still high."

"Where does it hurt, Vera?" He bent over me solicitously. I only whimpered in response and he went to call the doctor. When he returned moments later, it was with hurried steps and a grave countenance. "We need to take her to the hospital immediately." He stooped and took me into his strong arms. Turning to my grandma, he asked, "Can you stay with the children, Mom?"

"Of course, Victor," Grandma said.

Retrieving her Sunday bonnet from the hook, Mama placed it on her head and hastily told the other children goodbye before heading out the door with Dad and me.

My four-year-old brother Fred stood shyly in the doorway. " 'Bye, Vera."

" 'Bye," I squeaked. My throat was so sore that my words didn't come out right.

"Be good for Grandma, son." Dad's words were firm. Fred only nodded. I closed my eyes and waited, drifting in and out of my fog of pain.

At the Aultman Hospital in Canton, Ohio, I found myself under the bright lights of the emergency room, surrounded by bustling feet and hushed voices. The doctors and nurses were kind, but the needles and movement and lights during the examination hurt me. I was frightened and felt hot and cold by turns. When a nurse saw me shiver, she pulled a warm blanket over me. I cuddled deep and shut my eyes tight, trying to escape the pain.

Then the doctor came in, and I was uncovered and turned on my side.

They pushed my stiff legs upward and my head forward into a fetal position. I cried out in pain. "There, there. It will only be a few moments, honey," the nurse soothed as she stroked my hair. I tried to fight the painful position but a second nurse held me firmly in place. I felt a burning pain in my back, and tears dripped down my face. "Mama," I whimpered.

"Shh, honey. You can see your mama soon. Just hold still and be a good girl."

Those ten minutes seemed like a very long time. When the spinal tap was finally finished and I could lie back normally with the sheets snuggled over me, the tears were still running down my cheeks. The nurse brushed the tears from my face and tucked me in. "It's over, dear. Now you can rest."

I never heard the fateful words the doctor spoke to my parents. I only knew I wanted my mama and that she wasn't coming. But in another room he was gravely informing them that I needed to be admitted to the hospital immediately.

"I'm very sorry. The spinal tap came back positive for poliomyelitis. We'll make her as comfortable as possible. But I'm afraid we have an epidemic on our hands." It was 1952, and polio was on the rampage across the country. He shook his head sadly. After assuring them he would do all he could for me, he left them to absorb the news alone.

Meanwhile, I was being wheeled on a gurney up to the fifth floor of the hospital. Here in the solarium I joined other patients in the semi-isolated polio ward. A cheerful, bustling nurse immediately examined me. "Hello, what's your name, little one?"

Her smiling eyes were kind and her hands were gentle. She seemed to sense how fearful I was. "Vera," I squeaked.

"That's a lovely name, dearie. Open your mouth for me, okay?" She slipped a thermometer under my tongue and held my hand briefly between her warm fingers while she took my pulse. She was obviously efficient. But there was a comforting motherliness about her too. "Vera, my name is Mrs. Barbara Gaston and I'm going to be taking care of you for the next little while. You just lie still now and rest and get better real soon." She gave me another one of her lovely smiles before turning and bustling away.

I did as I was told and lay still. There was nothing else I could do. By now my whole trunk and arms were paralyzed. Only my neck and legs were still partially mobile. "Mama!" I cried out for the only comfort I knew as my breathing became labored.

The nurses were soon back, wrapping my tummy and arms in steaming hot wool cloths to loosen up my stiff muscles. I felt helplessly alone. "Mama," I pleaded.

The minutes ticked by, and my breathing grew ragged. As I fought for breath through a haze of pain, I heard Dr. Ream's voice. It seemed to come from a distance. "She's breathing with her abdominal muscles now instead of her chest muscles. We need to transfer her to the iron lung."

I felt my stiff, wooden body being lifted. They laid me on a bed inside a pressurized metal cylinder and adjusted the rubber foam around my neck. My head stuck out the end while the rest of my body was lost in that great metal tube. They closed the side ports and started the engine. I suddenly felt as if I could breathe again. I was so worn out, I closed my eyes.

Then she was beside me. "Vera." She murmured my name gently, and I opened my eyes with effort.

"Mama," I lisped weakly. She stroked my hair.

Then I felt another hand touch my face. It was Dad's work-roughened one. "Vera, we're here."

I looked up to see that both of them had tears in their eyes. I did not know the doctor had just informed them that I might not live through the night.

I closed my eyes wearily but through the fog I heard Dad say, "She's not going to die, Emma. I won't let her."

"She's in God's hands, Vic. It's going to be okay," I drifted away to the sound of Mama's voice as the tide of pain receded before the waves of exhaustion that engulfed me.

Beside me my parents waited and prayed.

CHAPTER 2

BATTLES BIG AND SMALL

All night long I awoke and slept in a fog of muffled noises, nightmares, and pain. I dreamed a great darkness was engulfing me, and I was so afraid I couldn't move or breathe. Then I heard Mama calling my name. I awoke to find her still there beside me, stroking my hair and whispering comfort in my ear. I drifted back into restless dreams.

"Mama, I can't breathe! Help me." I tried to sit up but couldn't. The paralysis in my lungs coupled with fluid buildup gave me a breathless, suffocating feeling, and I fought against it.

As I battled for my life, I little realized the anguished prayer battles my parents fought as they watched me through that long, dark night. I did not comprehend the battles heroic doctors and nurses across my country were fighting against the dreaded epidemic. I did not know that somewhere not many miles from where I lay breathing raggedly, a little boy my age lay buried, dead from the same frightful illness. Donald Hershberger's parents hadn't even been allowed to give their two-year-old son a funeral. The local health department allowed only a brief graveside service for the stricken family and community.

The polio epidemic that swept our country held many in dread. It was partial to none, and few if any understood the nature of polio's contagion. In 1952 scientists were only beginning to understand the virus and how it spread, and no known cure existed. Although only a small percentage of polio sufferers became paralyzed, the disease's epidemic tendencies struck terror in communities across the United States.

For me, the days following admittance to the hospital were a blur of fighting for breath, trying to sleep, and enduring pain. I hardly noticed what went on around me. Two things I did notice, though. I noticed when Barbara Gaston took care of me, and I knew when my parents were there and when they weren't.

Mama was there less often than Dad since the other children needed her as well. Every evening I would hear the heavy tread of my father's footsteps in the hall, even above the steady whooshing breaths of my iron lung. He always came, even after a day of hard work and chores. It brought a sense of security nothing else could, to see him come round the corner. The highlight of my days was to feel that large work-roughened hand touch my face and stroke my hair, and hear his usually booming voice ask gently, "How's my little Vera tonight?"

Sometimes as he sat by me through the long evening hours, he'd tell me stories, and other times we rested in contemplative silence. Just to have him near me was enough.

Sometimes, though, I was so sick I hardly knew he was there. My first two weeks in the hospital were especially this way. I contracted pneumonia from the fluid on my lungs and my weakened ability to cough. With the onset of infection, a high fever ensued, and again I fought for my life.

My lungs filled up with phlegm and I was unable to cough it up. I would choke and gag on the thick strings of mucus, sometimes turning gray as I struggled for breath. These times always brought doctors and nurses running. Desperately they would suction me out, pulling long, sticky ropes of phlegm from my mouth to free my airways.

Again I knew nothing of the battles being fought in the souls of my parents, or what battles were being fought in the heavenlies over their souls. Years later they told me about them, though.

Mama was a woman of faith. She grieved for my pain and helplessness, but her tender trust in God kept her strong. For my Dad, his strength was his downfall. He was determined that he would keep me alive.

One night after nearly two weeks in the hospital, I had a choking spell while Dad was there. I was so worn out and weak after my struggle that I could not respond when he called my name. I couldn't even open my eyes.

As he listened helplessly to my uneven, shallow breathing, my dad's mind traveled back to his own father's deathbed years before. It was a cold winter afternoon in 1938, just before Christmas, when his pa died.

The scene came back to him vividly, as if he were fifteen again: the somber faces of his older brothers, the tear-stained cheeks of his gentle mother, and the soft crying of his younger sister as they stood around the bedside. The cruel sound of that racking cough still sounded in his ears, painfully loud in the otherwise still room. Pa had coughed up blood again and again, and Victor was helpless to alleviate the illness.

Then came Christmas morning, three days later. It had been a cold, overcast day, the heavens leaden and silent with unspent snow. As a bitter wind blew through the crowd, the family and friends of Simeon Overholt gathered to lay him to rest. Victor's tears had been frozen inside him. He knew that now that his father was gone he'd have to be a man for his mother and sister, and men didn't cry.

If his pa had taught him anything, it was manliness. Every one of Simeon's nine sons respected him deeply, and none of them dared to question his authority. He was a man of few words, a serious disposition, and a strong work ethic. His words came back often to my dad in the following years of hard work and struggle. "Victor, if you don't try it, you will never know what you can do."

But now as Dad watched me, that unwanted feeling of inability assaulted him full force. He knew he couldn't do anything except pray. And his prayers didn't seem to go beyond the ceiling on this night. "God, you know what I want." Even through my weakness I heard him praying quietly beside me. "She has to live, God. Please make her well!"

I heard him get up. I didn't want him to leave me. I stirred but still could not open my eyes. I heard his heavy footsteps moving back and forth close beside me. Comforted, I drifted into an exhausted sleep.

Beside me, he continued to pray, begging God for my life. The battle within him was not just about me. It was about whether he could trust God with his own life as well. He'd always gone to church, and after a fashion he had followed God. But he'd never fully surrendered everything to Him.

If only I could help her! If only . . . he thought desperately. He willed his strength to be my strength. *I will not let her die.* More than ever before, he longed to take me into his strong arms. But his holding me now would mean certain death.

Perhaps it was this parallel that broke through to my dad about the choice before him. If he held me and comforted me, I would die. I had to be in the iron lung to breathe. So, too, he longed to hold onto my life and make me live, but only God could give life. Outside of God, life was impossible for me and for him as well.

It hit him with renewed force. "I am helpless to help her. Lord . . . I can't do this . . . anymore." His heart broke and, burying his face in his hands, he wept. I never heard my dad cry. I was wrapped in sleep. But Someone Else was well aware of the struggle and very present to help in this time of need. It was a moment when heaven held its breath, and the Father waited. Victor felt the weight of his stubbornness, and the anguish of death crushing in on his soul. Unmindful of anything around him, he fell to his knees.

"Oh, God, please . . . you know what I want from you."

The tears turned to muffled sobs and his broad shoulders shook with restrained emotion. "But, Lord, I can't fight anymore. I can't save her. I can't save myself. Lord, not my will—" For a moment he choked on the words, fighting to open his hand and release all that was dear to him into the unseen hands of God. As if this unseen hand on his shoulder strengthened him, he whispered the words, "But thine be done. Whatever you choose . . . I will . . . accept. I surrender all to you, Father. Everything."

At these words a strange emptiness filled him, as if it had taken everything he had to say them. But even as he noted this, warmth began to flow through him. Buoyancy and peace seemed to wrap around his wounded soul, and he knew without a doubt that this time his prayer had been heard.

Rising from his knees and wiping a few stray tears from his weathered face, he looked at me. He touched my head gently and leaned closer to listen to me breathe. It was still the same as it had been for weeks. But somehow he was at peace. Everything looked different from before.

Feeling dazed, he sat down slowly and resumed his vigil. He thought of the years since his father's death and how he'd often wondered about the words the minister spoke at the funeral. The minister had said something about a "living hope," and for years Dad hadn't really known what those words meant. Eventually he'd gained head knowledge of them, of course. But it had never sunk into his heart. Now in this sacred moment he suddenly knew, in the deepest part of his being, what it was to have a "living hope." With that heart surrender to God, he had found not only peace, but new life as well.

I whimpered in my sleep, and he got up to comfort me. It was getting late and he would soon have to leave for the night. But he wanted to wait until the nurse came again. Suddenly he realized something had changed. Was he imagining it? Something in my breathing seemed different. It wasn't as raspy.

He stood gazing down at me for some time, wondering if his observations could possibly be true, hardly daring to hope. When the night nurse came in soon after, she confirmed what he was thinking. "She is certainly resting much easier than she was a few hours ago," she rejoiced cautiously.

The next morning Dr. Graham came in as usual. When he noted that I seemed less labored in my breathing, he did a thorough check-up. When he finished he smiled at Dad. "She's definitely better this morning. If all goes well from here, we may be on the road to recovery."

When Dad told me "Good morning," a special twinkle shone in his eyes. I was even well enough to eat a bit of breakfast! I didn't know that he was celebrating more than one kind of "new life" that morning. I only knew he was happy, and that made me happy. I smiled back at him. It was the first time I'd smiled in days.

~

"Aren't you hungry, Vera?" the nurse coaxed.

"Thocolate milk," I lisped decidedly. I was just learning to speak English, since we mostly spoke Pennsylvania Dutch in our home. I understood much more English than I spoke, but two words I knew before I came to the hospital described my favorite food item.

The nurse sighed and shook her head. "You can't live on chocolate milk, dearie. It makes mucus in your lungs if you drink too much of it. You're as light as a feather, and if you don't eat proper food you won't gain strength. That would be a shame now, wouldn't it?"

"Banana." I watched her face mischievously.

"Eat this bite of vegetables first and then you can have a bite of banana," the nurse bargained. She smiled when I reluctantly opened my mouth to comply. "That's right. Now you'll grow big and strong," she cheered.

I grimaced and swallowed the peas and carrots grudgingly. Now for that promised bite of banana! I was quickly learning to get what I wanted from the nurses. They all seemed fond of me and almost doted on me.

But one thing I refused to do well was to eat, even if my favorite nurse Mrs. Gaston was coaxing me. I hated trying to eat. I wasn't moving about at all, which left me with very little appetite. I had always tended to be a particular eater even as a tiny child, and now the uphill battle to get enough nutrients into me was a daily cross for my kind caregivers.

"Vera, if you could choose one kind of food to eat all the time, which one would you choose? What is your very favorite thing to eat?" Dr. Graham was doing the normal daily rounds, and he must have been worried about how thin I had become.

I looked up and gave him a toothy grin. "Popthicles." I had never known what these were before I came to the hospital, but in their desperation to get me to eat, the nurses had tried nearly everything. Popsicles had been a rare success.

Dr. Graham ordered popsicles to be delivered to the polio ward on a daily basis. How I loved to lick that colored ice with my tongue, the sweet fruit-flavored liquid running down my chin. Later, at my pleading, all the other children in the ward received one daily as well. It became a bright spot in our daily routine.

Recovery was tedious and often painful. Every day was filled with the routines of meals, exercises, naps, and hot packing. Hot packing was my least favorite activity. It happened five times around the clock, and every child in the ward hated those hot, itchy, woolen cloths. Accordingly we created a sort of game among ourselves to raise group morale in preparation for the ordeal.

"How are the hot packs tonight?" Matthew would ask pensively.

"Oohh, hot!" Sarah would exclaim expressively.

"Ohhh . . ." A collective groan would go up from all of us children in the ward as the hot pack steamer rolled on to the next patient.

When it was my turn, I always turned my face away from the nurse to pout. She'd wrap my arms, legs, shoulders, torso, and back in the steaming hot cloths and then cover them with plastic to keep in the heat and moisture. She did all this through the ports of my iron lung.

"Only a half hour, dear, and then we can take them off again," she'd say cheerfully as she bustled on to the next patient. I still didn't look at her. And when she came to take them off I always felt hot and itchy and grumpy, even though the stiffness and soreness in my limbs and body were temporarily relieved.

The paralysis damage to my lungs was extensive, and I struggled to be weaned from the iron lung far more than some of the other patients did. However, little by little, first by leaving one of the ports open on the side of the lung to reduce the pressure inside, and then gradually working me up to several minutes at a time outside the lung, I began to learn to breathe a little bit on my own.

One morning Mrs. JoAnn Littlefield was doing my care. She smiled at me broadly and announced, "Vera, today the doctor said you can try using the rocking bed. Would you like that?" I looked at her and nodded. "Yes, please."

She chuckled. "Good for you, Vera. You are learning to use your manners quite nicely."

Her compliment made me feel warm and happy inside, and I was eager to please her as she opened the iron lung and got me ready to go on the rocking bed.

Set up in the hall, the bed's seesaw motion used gravity to force air in and out of a patient's lungs. At first I felt a bit breathless and held onto the nurse tightly with my legs. "Mrs. Littlefield, I don't want to," I said desperately.

"Of course you do, Vera. It's okay. Just let me get you started and it will be easier to breathe." She strapped me onto the bed and started the motion. Just as she had promised, it did get easier to breathe. I gave her a tremulous smile.

"It's okay, Vera. I'll be right here to help you. Just think, if you learn to do this, you can spend more time outside the iron lung."

I loved any challenge, but the feeling of being weaned from my beloved "Emerton," as I called the bright yellow Emerson iron lung, was hard for me. I had been in it for three months and it brought me a great sense of security, especially in my weakened condition.

The Emerson was a canister-shaped respirator that worked on the principle of a vacuum. I was sealed inside the canister from the neck down, my body resting on a bed fitted on metal tracks that could be rolled out if desired. When the electric motor at the foot of the bed was started, it sucked out most of the air and caused my lungs to expand. Then air was compressed into the canister and my lungs exhaled.

When I began to show signs of wear during the rocking bed sessions, Mrs. Littlefield or another nurse would encourage me. "Just a few minutes more and then we'll put you back in your Emerson." And so it was that little by little I learned the rocking bed was nothing to fear. Rather, like my "Emerton," it was my friend. On my fourth birthday, that November, the nurses took a picture of me "standing" on the rocking bed.

The heavy tread of Dad's footsteps in the hall every evening was the highlight of my daily existence. When he entered the ward, I always greeted him eagerly. He was friendly to the other children in the ward too, teasing and laughing with them as he passed their beds. He always took a seat beside my iron lung and listened to me talk about my day, smiling and nodding and sometimes stroking my hair gently.

Mama didn't come to visit daily. She was expecting her sixth child and was too weary by the end of the day to come. But she came as often as she could, and when she did I clung to every moment with her. One night before we parted, my mother gave me her special smile and I knew she had a secret to tell me. I waited anxiously to know what it was.

"Vera, when the baby is born, would you like to help name it?" This was a way she and my father had decided they could help me feel included in the arrival of my new sibling, even though I couldn't be at home like the rest of my sisters and brothers.

"Oh, yes!" I felt so happy inside that I wanted to sing. "Baby Lena is cute. But I'm glad we get another baby." Without a second thought I knew what I would name this new baby sister. "And I'm going to name it Barbara. Because Mrs. Gaston is the one I like the most."

In the following weeks, it was my greatest delight to tell everyone who stopped to chat with me about my newly acquired privilege. "I'm gonna name her and her name is going to be Barbara," I would announce emphatically. And then by way of explanation I would add, "Because that's Mrs. Gaston's name and I like her the most."

Besides my dad's daily visits, Mrs. Gaston's cheery care was the mainstay of my daily routine, and I loved her with all my little heart.

But I was young and changeable, and I could be childishly vindictive. One small battle with lasting results was fought the day my baby sister was born.

It was midway through my bath and I was feeling particularly out of sorts that day, which was unusual for me. "Vera, it's time to do your leg exercises," Mrs. Gaston coached me cheerfully. The nurse's aide tried to move my foot accordingly, but I pulled away. "Come now, Vera. Move it like this," the nurse's aide coaxed.

I felt the rebellion rising within me at my own helplessness and the discomfort everything seemed to cause. I turned my lips into a pout. "Not gonna do it," I stated defiantly. "Not gonna do it!"

"Come on, Vera. Where's my cheerful girl this morning?" Mrs. Gaston remonstrated gently. "We have to do your exercises. But it won't take long and then they'll be done. Okay?"

"Not gonna do it," I repeated saucily.

Mrs. Gaston clucked sympathetically. "But we have to do it whether you want to or not, Vera. You don't have a choice." With that they began to work my legs and feet in the warm water. I sulkily turned my head away from them and sniffled miserably.

Just then Mrs. Littlefield walked into the room. Seeing their predicament, she shook her head sympathetically and asked, "Is Mrs. Gaston making you do hard things, Vera?"

"Yes, she is." My eyes were filled with unshed tears. One drop ran down my cheek, and Mrs. Gaston gently brushed it away.

"Don't meddle now, JoAnn. She's just having a difficult day," Mrs. Gaston explained efficiently.

Mrs. Littlefield smiled understandingly and then winked at me. "Well, I just got a piece of news that might cheer you up a bit, Vera. Can you guess what it is?" Her eyes twinkled merrily.

"Dunno. What is it, Mrs. Littlefield?" I asked mournfully.

"You have a baby sister!" Mrs. Littlefield cheered.

My frown turned to an instant smile. "I'm gonna name her!" I shouted.

Then, remembering my grievance, I glared at Mrs. Gaston and shot out my chin defiantly. "I'm gonna name her and I'm gonna name her JoAnn," I finished triumphantly. I looked at Mrs. Littlefield for approval, but she had exited the room hastily to hide her laughter, leaving Mrs. Gaston to finish her battle alone.

CHAPTER 3

HOSPITAL DAYS AND FRIENDS

"I can see you, Nancy," I giggled.

"I can see you too, Vera." Nancy waggled a finger at me. I stuck out my tongue and made a face in the mirror above my head.

Nancy was seven years old and wasn't in an iron lung. She was just in a regular bed. But after nearly a year in the hospital, I was still in the iron lung a good portion of my days, especially for naps and nighttime. Often after several hours on the rocking bed in the hall, I was ready to rest in my iron lung as well.

Over every iron lung was a mounted mirror so the child in the iron lung could see the child in the bed across from him or her. It helped entertain us and pass the hours as we held "mirror conversations." But at the moment we were not supposed to be entertaining ourselves; we were supposed to be taking our naps.

"Nancy, I want to tell you a secret."

"What is it?" Her tone was hushed and eager.

I smiled at her teasingly. "I can tell you only if you promise not to tell the others," I whispered loudly.

"Of course I won't, Vera. I always keep your secrets. Come on, tell me," she pleaded impatiently.

"Mama is coming tonight to read to me," I whispered importantly. "If you are really quiet, you can listen too."

"Girls!"

We both jumped guiltily as the nurse stuck her head around the doorway. Her face was stern. "Aren't you two supposed to be sleeping?"

We didn't dare look at each other. We nodded mutely.

"All right, then. No more talking until you've had some rest. Do you understand?"

We nodded again, and she made a quick round of the ward and left.

The nurses were good to us. They tried to make life as family-oriented and pleasant as possible for their little patients. But they also made us mind our manners and keep the rules. Many of the children didn't see their parents daily, and the nurses were like surrogate mothers or aunties to us all, making us say "please" and "thank you" and comforting us when we cried from pain.

That night Mama came as she had promised, bringing with her a new book someone had sent in a sunshine package for me. It was a beautifully illustrated edition of nursery tales, and although few of the stories were new to me, I loved hearing them read to me.

"What shall we read tonight, Vera?" Mama reached out a hand to stroke my hair, her brown eyes tender in her mild face.

"Jack and the Beanstalk," I decided quickly. "I like how the beanstalk grows so fast—it's like a miracle!"

Mama smiled and thumbed through the pages until she found the story I had requested. She read expressively about the desperate boy and his mother, the magic beanstalk, and the bad giant.

I listened eagerly as she read, holding my breath during the scary parts. Nancy sat on the end of her bed with her eyes fixed on Mama's face.

When she came to the part of the story about how Jack escaped from the giant, I let out my breath in relief. And when Jack was finally able to provide food for his mother with the hen that laid golden eggs, I smiled broadly.

This story was followed by "The Ugly Duckling" and two others before Mama put the book away. "One more, Mama, please?" I pleaded.

"I'll come again soon and we'll read some more," she assured me.

I sighed in regret.

"Thank you, Mrs. Overholt!" Nancy exclaimed. "I do so love a good story." Mama smiled at her, and I suddenly remembered my manners.

"Thank you, Mama."

She stooped to kiss me on the forehead. "I love you, Vera. Sleep well tonight."

"Good night, Mama."

"Good night, Mrs. Overholt."

I looked at Nancy dreamily, feeling suddenly tired. "It was fun, wasn't it?"

"Yes, I hope she comes again soon," Nancy agreed, yawning. "I like your mama very much."

The children in the ward were all family for each other. We competed and cheered for each other by turns and sometimes we fought outright, just like any normal group of children. Nancy and I were especially close because our beds were close together, and Nancy called the nurse for me whenever I needed or wanted one.

One day when the nurses were preparing Nancy to stand on her own for the first time since her illness, she panicked. "No, no! Please don't let go," she pled with them.

Hearing my friend's distress, I felt a great compassion for her. The nurses had taught us by their own cheerful coaching how to encourage each other in difficult moments of recovery.

From across the room I squeaked, "You can do it! Nancy, you can do it!"

Nancy's frightened eyes met mine and for an instant she wavered. "You can! I know it!" I cheered.

She nodded tremblingly, and I watched fear give way to determination as she agreed. "Okay, I'll try."

For several seconds she stood alone. And when she collapsed back against the nurse, a full-hearted cheer went up from all over the ward.

"You did it!" I squeaked excitedly. "I knew you could, Nancy. Good for you!"

It was indeed a moment of progress. When the nurse turned to leave after helping Nancy back to bed, I saw tears in her eyes.

"Why are you sad, Mrs. Littlefield?" I asked puzzled.

"Oh, Vera," she laughed shakily. "I'm not sad, honey. Those are happy tears."

I did not understand then that most days the nurses were happy if the movement in a toe or finger increased for a patient. But more than that, her tears were caused by the beauty of a common love shared by a group of suffering children.

Every morning one of the nurse aides combed out my long hair. This was one of my greatest trials. On several occasions a nurse talked about cutting my hair short so it would be easy to care for. "You can't cut my hair!" I exclaimed indignantly on such occasions. "You can't do that. My dad would be unhappy with you."

But I certainly complained while they combed out the snarls. The nurses would cock their heads and say, "Remember what we told you about your hair, Vera."

And I would sigh and respond, "I know. Beauty must suffer."

"That's right. Beauty must suffer." And I would resign myself to the ordeal without further complaining.

One day when one of the nurses had a few spare moments, she braided pink ribbons into my hair. I admired them in my mirror adoringly. "Thank you. I look beautiful, don't I?"

"Yes, Vera. Very beautiful." She smiled.

That night when Dad visited, Mrs. Gaston was doing my evening care as usual. Dad took one look at my hair and turned soberly. "Mr. Overholt, is something wrong?" Mrs. Gaston asked.

My dad was a man who didn't mince words. He got straight to the point. "What is going on here, Mrs. Gaston?" He looked directly at my pink ribbons, as if accusing them of a crime.

"What? Do you mean Vera's hair, Mr. Overholt? Don't you like it?"

Dad was silent for a moment, and then he looked Mrs. Gaston in the eye and explained quietly, "Well, how would you feel if wearing your hair like that was against what your family believed, and you came in and found your daughter's hair like that?"

Mrs. Gaston nodded respectfully. "I understand now, Mr. Overholt. I understand."

"Thank you. I knew I could trust you." Dad closed the conversation firmly, but there was a warmth in his voice that I didn't miss.

Without a word she removed the ribbons quickly and then left us to spend our normal visiting hours together. I felt slightly disappointed about the ribbons. But I knew my parents held a high respect for Mrs. Gaston because she held a mutual respect for them. I loved her all the more for it.

As the days passed, I grew impatient to expand my range of activities. With my fingers too paralyzed to use, I reverted to using my toes as fingers early on. Even in the first few months of my stay, I learned to play doll with my bears and babies in my iron lung. I would take my toes and line them up and cover them with a blanket. I could not see them, but I could feel them and imagine what they looked like.

One day after I had graduated to a bed for part of each day, I found I could hold a crayon between my toes and color pictures. When I had finished a brightly colored rainbow with puffy purple and orange clouds, I waited for my favorite nurse to come to the ward. "Look, Mrs. Gaston. I made this page especially for you." I held it out eagerly to her, my heart happy in the thought of her pleasure.

"Why, thank you, Vera! This is beautiful! It's so carefully done, with all the color inside the lines." She stooped over and kissed me. "I am so proud of you." She smiled and I glowed under the praise.

After a year, Mrs. Gaston was still my favorite nurse. Despite my naming of my baby sister after Mrs. Littlefield, my grudge had been short-lived, and Mrs. Gaston now held her place more firmly than ever in my heart. I always knew that if someone else got a gift or a new toy, all I had to do was ask Mrs. Gaston and she would get me one as well. In some ways she spoiled me. But I never had any qualms about this.

A few weeks later I saw Nancy cutting out shapes with a scissors. "Nancy, please let me try," I begged.

"You can't," she responded matter-of-factly. "You have to have fingers to cut with, Vera. I can cut something for you, though. What shape do you want?"

I shook my head determinedly. "No, Nancy. I want to try it myself. Please, give me the scissors."

Shaking her head doubtfully, she passed me the scissors and a sheet of paper with shapes on it. Carefully grasping the handles between my toes, I picked up the paper with my other foot and began to cut. My first shape was ragged, but I felt a sense of triumph as I looked up at Nancy and grinned. "See? I told you I could do it."

She shrugged. "I guess you can. That's pretty good, Vera."

I honed my cutting skills from then on and was soon cutting as perfectly as anyone with hands could cut. When the nurses found me doing it, they marveled together. "How do you do that, Vera?"

"I just do it," I responded matter-of-factly.

I heard Mrs. Littlefield commenting to another nurse as they left the room. "I think she'll go far in life. It doesn't appear this handicap is going to hold her back from much."

One day in August, just a year after my hospitalization, my grandma came to visit me. She didn't come often and it was always special when she did. "Grandma, do you want to see me throw a ball?" I asked excitedly. It was my newest acquired skill and I loved to share it with anyone who would watch.

She watched me throw the ball with my feet, and her eyes twinkled. "Well, look at that," she praised. She told me about the canning season and how the peaches and tomatoes were cooling in jars on the counters at home. She told me about how big Lena had grown since I had gone away. I told her about life in the hospital and introduced her to Nancy. Then it was time for her to go. Her cheek was soft against mine as she said goodbye.

I little dreamt it would be the last time I would ever see my beloved grandma again. That night she passed away quietly at home. I would not know what

I had lost until I came home and no longer heard her cheerful tread on the kitchen floor or her strong voice calling my name. For my parents, though, this was a heavy blow on top of what they were already facing.

For Dad, the staggering number of medical bills had begun to take their toll. He worked hard, rising long before dawn to chore in the dairy barn, eating breakfast at 6:00 with his family. Leaving for a long day on the mason crew, he returned in the evening to milk cows a second time, eat a quick supper with his family, and head back to the hospital for his evening visit with me.

At one point he considered selling the farm to pay for the expenses they continued to acquire for my care. However, God mercifully saw fit to provide in other ways. As is often the case, communities of believers rose up to help in this time of need. As my story became more widely known among friends and relatives, churches across the United States sent various sums of money to help our family cover their continued bills.

Help came in other tangible ways as well. One day the bishop of Hartville Conservative Mennonite Church, Roman Miller, called Dad and asked him to drop by about a piece of business. When Dad arrived, Roman handed him a pair of keys and a title and led him to a Chevy car. "I know you are in need of a vehicle right now, especially with all the visits you are making to the hospital. Several churches contributed in purchasing this car. It's a gift for you and your family."

Dad, though a man of strong reserve, nearly cried with gratitude. "Thank you. You'll never know how much this means." His parting handclasp was warm and firm, conveying what words could not.

For me, though, life outside the hospital walls had little impact. I badly wanted to meet my baby sister, and I often missed my mama. Otherwise, I was mostly content with the small joys and triumphs of everyday life.

CHAPTER 4

HOME AGAIN

November came again and with it, my fifth birthday. I had been counting the days till the thirteenth for weeks, and Mrs. Gaston helped me keep track every day. Now it was Friday morning. The long-awaited day had finally arrived. I awoke with a sense of excitement and anticipation.

"Happy birthday, Vera!" Mrs. Littlefield greeted me exuberantly. "How's the birthday girl this morning?" She seemed to have a special twinkle in her eye, and I was curious if she had something to tell me.

"I'm good, Mrs. Littlefield. I can't wait to eat cake."

She grinned. "How about what you are going to wear today?" she asked. "Shouldn't it be something special for such a special day?"

"I don't have something new, Mrs. Littlefield. I can wear my blue dress. I like that one."

"How about starting your birthday with a surprise from all the nurses?"

From all over the ward the nurses and nurse aides gathered around my yellow Emerson with big smiles on their faces and sang "Happy Birthday."

"Now for your surprise," Mrs. Littlefield announced. She reached into a bag and pulled out something yellow. "Do you like it, Vera?"

I squealed in pleasure. "A new dress!" The sun-colored dress had a rounded collar and a wide skirt. "It's pretty! Thank you so much!"

"We love you, Vera!" the nurses chorused.

"Shall we see how it fits?" asked Mrs. Littlefield. I needed no coaxing. Soon I was sitting dressed in my birthday finery with a big smile on my face. It fit perfectly and I couldn't have dreamt of a happier way to start my day.

That evening both Mama and Daddy came to visit me. "Happy Birthday, Vera!" Mama hugged me. "We brought you a cake to celebrate."

I looked at the white frosted cake with delicate pink edges. "It's beautiful," I breathed. "Can I save it?"

"I thought maybe you'd want us to eat it with you. We can have a little party if you want. But if you'd like to save it, that would be fine too." Her eyes twinkled a little. "Do you think it's too pretty to eat?"

I nodded and Dad chuckled. "You're thin enough, Vera. There will be more cakes for other years. I think you should have a nice big piece right now." Whatever Dad said was what I wanted to do. I changed my mind, and we all ate cake and shared the remainder with the nurses and the other children. It was a party to remember. When Mama and Dad said good night at bedtime, I lay for a long time after they were gone, simply savoring the memories of the day.

The next day was Saturday. Sometimes on Saturdays Reverend Corman, a minister from the community, came to visit the children in the polio ward. He was one of my favorite regular visitors. His graying hair and kindly smile always made me feel comfortable and friendly.

All the children gathered around him, and he smiled jovially at all of us in turn. "What shall it be tonight, children? Story or poetry first?" He was a great lover of good poetry and often quoted it to us.

"Please say the sky poem from last week," Nancy begged eagerly.

"Ah, the poem by Emily Dickinson: 'There Is Another Sky.' It's a beautiful title, isn't it, Nancy?" She nodded and we all listened quietly as he launched into an eloquent recitation.

"There is another sky,
Ever serene and fair,
And there is another sunshine,
Though it be darkness there;
Never mind faded forests, Austin,
Never mind silent fields—
Here is a little forest,
Whose leaf is ever green;
Here is a brighter garden,
Where not a frost has been;
In its unfading flowers
I hear the bright bee hum:
Prithee, my brother,
Into my garden come!"

"Reverend Corman, what doeth 'prithee' mean?" I asked.

"That's a good question, Vera." He smiled. *Prithee* is an old English way of saying 'please.' Now for a story. Who is going to choose our story tonight?"

Matthew's hand shot up. "David and Goliath."

"Ah. A hero story from the best book of all," Reverend Corman approved. "Does everyone else agree?" After a bit of squabble and discussion among ourselves, we agreed that Matthew should have his choice. Any story Reverend Corman told was good.

"All right, then. Let's begin." He cleared his throat, letting our suspense build a bit. "A long time ago there was a shepherd boy who took care of his father's sheep. He was a brave, goodhearted boy who often sang as he did his work. The boy's name was David. One day when David was out leading his sheep to water, he heard a loud growl. Without any warning, a great big lion leaped from a rock ledge above him and pounced on one of his lambs. David had a long wooden staff in his hands. He was a strong boy as well as a good shepherd. He knew he needed to protect that little lamb." We all waited tensely as he told how the boy attacked the lion and killed it, saving the wounded lamb from its ferocious jaws.

We tensed as he talked about the big bear that came, and we rejoiced when he again rescued his little sheep from danger. Best of all was the part about Goliath and how with a sling and a stone, the fearful enemy of a whole army was defeated. "This boy knew how to fight all these fierce things because he trusted in God to help him," Reverend Corman concluded. "As you grow up to be men and women you will also need God to help you. But you don't have to wait till you are older to ask Him to help you. He's with you even now." His face was serious and we all nodded gravely, feeling the import of his words.

Glancing at his watch, he rose a bit stiffly from his chair. "It's almost bedtime for young folks," he smiled. "I best be getting home to bed myself." And then as was his usual custom, he bid us good night with the words from Shakespeare's famous *Romeo and Juliet*. "Good night, good night! Parting is such sweet sorrow that I shall say . . ."

". . . Good night till it be morrow," we all chorused in unison with him.

"Good night, Reverend Corman. Thank you for coming! Come again soon!" We watched him go down the hall, and then the scramble to get ready for bed began as usual.

Social workers whom we children called "gray ladies" also came to read to us regularly, and the Canton Public Library provided a small library of books for us children. They also sent librarians on occasion to read to us. All those wonderful stories helped pass the long, tedious hours in the ward. This early exposure to so many books formed my lifelong love for reading and literature.

Now that my birthday was past, the next event I anticipated was Christmas. That is, until the day Dad announced that they would soon be bringing me home. I could hardly fathom the news when he told me. "Really? You mean I can come home to stay?" I exclaimed in wonder.

At the next thought, though, my joy melted away. "How will I breathe?" I asked anxiously.

"We'll have an iron lung for you in the living room, just like you have here," he explained. "Would you like that?"

"Oh, yes!" I wanted to dance for joy. "When can I come home, Dad?"

"We'd all like to have you home for Christmas. We've missed having you with us."

And so it was that three days before Christmas, on a snowy Tuesday morning, I was carried out in my father's strong arms to the waiting car. I'd said all my goodbyes to the nurses that morning, and with the typical eagerness of early childhood, I felt little sadness at parting. I was sure I would see them again, and more than anything else I wanted to be home.

The ride home was strange to me. I watched the world go by outside the windows of the car with wonder. It had been almost a year and a half since I'd entered the hospital. When Dad carried me into the house, my siblings all stood around me shyly, like small strangers. I felt strangely shy myself.

They quickly set up the iron lung in the living room, and I was placed inside so I could rest after the strenuous ride. "Vera, let me know if there is anything I can do to help you." Ruth seemed more sage and grown up than she had when I left. I nodded and looked from face to face curiously. Fred was taller than he had been when I left home, and Leon's chubby toddler face was thinner now. Lena surprised me the most. She wasn't a baby anymore. I gave her a special smile to remind her of our old friendship. She grinned back uncertainly.

"And this is JoAnn," Mama gave me her special smile and held my baby sister up for me to see. She was about the same age Lena had been when I'd contracted polio.

"This is your sister, Vera. She gave you your name." JoAnn looked at me and my iron lung with wide, curious eyes, sucking her fingers thoughtfully. She seemed uncertain what to think. I, on the other hand, loved her instantly.

We'd soon make up for lost time, but for now I needed to rest. "Is this comfortable?" Ruth arranged my pillow under my head and smoothed my hair. I nodded gratefully.

Just as I was drifting off to sleep I heard someone whisper, "Good night, Vera." It was Lena.

"Does it hurt to be in that thing?" she asked.

"No. It helps me." I smiled at her sleepily. "I'll play with you when I wake up," I promised.

"With your dolls and bears?" she asked hopefully. I nodded, and her dark eyes shone happily.

Without another word, she turned and scampered away. I closed my eyes again. I was so tired. But it was good to be home! I had been in the hospital for five hundred days.

CHAPTER 5

GOODBYE IS NOT FOREVER

"Goodbye, Vera! We'll miss you!" Ruth assured me.

"I'll come and see you!" Lena added eagerly.

I had been at home for three months, and now Mama was preparing me for the drive to Cleveland Hospital. The doctors at Aultman Hospital had recommended Cleveland City Hospital's Toomey Pavilion as the most advanced option for continuing my necessary therapy, further surgeries, and bracing. Toomey Pavilion was known as one of the best regional respiratory care and rehabilitation centers in the country. And my parents wanted the best possible option of care for me.

My first reaction when I found out I would be returning to the hospital was a bleak one. I had just begun to enjoy and fit in with life at home with my siblings, and I did not welcome the prospect of the long hours in a hospital bed and iron lung away from home.

"But the doctor said we can bring you home to be with the family on weekends," my dad reassured me.

"And we'll come to see you," Fred offered consolingly.

"We will," Leon agreed.

Baby JoAnn just sucked her fingers and looked at me.

I tried to be cheerful as I said goodbye, but I didn't feel cheerful. I knew I would miss them, especially Lena. As we pulled away from the house, a tear slid down my cheek. I looked out the window at the new green of early springtime. Mama saw the tear and brushed it away.

"There now, Vera. Don't cry. You'll be just fine. You'll make new friends and learn how to walk and how to eat on your own. Won't you like that?"

I nodded a little. "Maybe." I wasn't sure.

Cleveland City Hospital was a massive compound of brick buildings. I felt lost as I looked forlornly at its imposing structures. Dad got me out of the car and carried me into the appropriate building where I was checked in and taken up to the polio children's ward on a gurney.

Several young nurses bustled about getting me settled. I watched their every move with a careful intensity. They wore starched white caps just like the nurses at Aultman had. One of them had dark, lively eyes and quick movements. The other one seemed shy, and her cheeks dimpled when she smiled. I smiled back at her. I wanted to make friends. But I still felt lonely and lost. Neither of these nurses was like Mrs. Gaston. When Dad and Mama came to say good night, I wished they could stay with me.

∽

"Time to rise and shine, Vera!" It was a Tuesday morning a week after my admittance to Cleveland, and I was quickly settling into the daily routine. "Breakfast first and then you get to choose a dress. Which one would you like to wear today? Blue or yellow?" the nurse asked cheerfully.

"Blue," I decided. "Is Paul awake?" My new friend was the boon of my first long days in the hospital. He and I had quickly fallen into conversation the second day I was there, and he always seemed able to answer my questions, even when he was very tired. He had to be in an iron lung all the time, just as

I had at the beginning of my illness. But he always smiled. And he told wonderful stories.

"Yes, dear." The nurse smiled down at me as she helped me eat my porridge. "He's been up for a bit already. After your exercises you can visit with him, I am sure."

My schedule included hours of therapy and meals and rests. But after breakfast I always talked to Paul at least for a little while. Today he seemed more chipper than usual. I knew he was happy to see me by the way he smiled at me.

"Hi, Vera."

"Hi, Paul!" Any shyness in me had melted within the first day. Paul was like an older brother to me. His twelve-year-old wisdom and gentleness made me feel safe with him.

"Do you like being in the iron lung?" I asked curiously.

"It helps me breathe, I guess. So in that way, yes."

"You aren't tired of it?"

"Well, maybe. But sometime I'll get out and walk again. You have to keep hope."

"I know you can do it sometime," I said cheerily. "I like the iron lung at night. But I am glad to be out for most of the time now. Maybe sometime you can play with me. I would like that." He nodded.

I cocked my head to one side. "Why do people get sick, Paul?"

"I can't say for sure, Vera. I guess it's just a part of life. I'm sorry you have to be sick, though. It really is a shame."

I shook my head. "No, Paul, it's not. Because I met you, you know, and now we're friends. I would be sad if I didn't know you."

He smiled his slow smile. "That's true, Vera. You're right that good things can come out of something hard, even though sometimes they seem like bad things to us at first."

"But I really miss my family. I miss Lena the most. And you miss your little brother the most, right?" Paul had told me all about his big family with lots of siblings. His parents were often there with him and sometimes one of his older siblings came. You had to be twelve to visit a patient in the ward, though.

None of my siblings were that old yet.

He looked thoughtful for a moment. "That's true, Vera. But if you can get better, you can go home and live with them again all the time, right?"

I nodded happily. "And I'm not so lonely with you here."

"Vera, it's time to practice on the standing board." The nurse was beside the bed, ready to move me for my next therapy session.

"See you later, Paul."

"See ya, little pal."

Having spent most of my time on my back for a year and a half, learning to adjust to a sitting or standing position was not easy. The standing board made me dizzy at first. I was strapped onto it, much like I had been on the rocking bed. But the board didn't rock. It was slowly tilted upward until I was in a standing position. Gradually my body began to adjust to being upright again.

Adjustments were not always easy at the hospital. Some of the goals were my own. Others I found impractical for how I lived and coped. My biggest goal was to graduate from the iron lung to a chest respirator. The medical staff endlessly encouraged me in this.

Another thing the doctors taught me early at Cleveland was how to "frog breathe." It was a new technique also known as glossopharyngeal breathing. When I told Paul about frog breathing and tried to tell him what the technical term for it was, he laughed and helped me pronounce it until I could say it almost perfectly.

My diaphragm was totally paralyzed. But I could force more air into my lungs by lowering my tongue and trapping a bubble of air, then capping my tongue to the roof of my mouth, opening my trachea, and compressing the air into the trachea with my tongue. I learned slowly. It was hard and many patients gave up. I was determined, but found it hard to practice in front of others. Dr. Eiben, my physician, was especially good with children and seemed to sense my need for privacy.

"Don't look," I would say.

His square face would spread into a bemused smile. "All right, Vera. I'll turn my back and then I want to hear you try. Okay?"

I'd nod my agreement, and he knew by the *gup-gup-gup* sounds that I was practicing.

"Very good, Vera. Try that again now." Without seeing his face I knew he was smiling. I could hear it in his tone.

It would take several years before I actually mastered the technique. Eventually, though, I would regain enough breath through this practice to be able to sing and even yell a bit.

The splints were my least favorite part of the program at Cleveland, especially the leg splints that forced my legs into a standing position. And the ugly brown orthopedic shoes I had to wear! One day I asked the nurse about them. "If I have to have shoes, why can't I have red strap ones like the other girls?" Red strap shoes were something I sorely longed for but never received during my stay at the hospital. I didn't ever think about the fact that my parents wouldn't have wanted me to wear red shoes. I only knew I hated the ugly brown ones.

Splints were fastened to my fingers to keep them from curling. My fingers and wrists and arms were rigorously exercised, and the steaming woolen hot pack treatments continued as well. Slowly I learned to feed myself tediously.

I was given a neck brace and a metal corset as well. These, along with my leg braces, gave me the ability to begin to walk a little. One day I was photographed for a March of Dimes poster. Sitting in my wheelchair, I smiled into the camera, unafraid of the flashing light. I wasn't afraid to be the center of attention. And though I knew little about March of Dimes, I knew that money had come from them to help pay our medical bills. I had overheard my parents talking once about the campaign that helped provide funds for polio research and polio patient rehabilitation.

I made many friends besides Paul. All of the children interacted more or less. But I did not confine myself to the children's ward. Sometimes I walked to the adults' ward.

"Ah, here comes little Vera!" Bill would cheer. He and Bob liked to play card games together. One day when Bob was out doing therapy, Bill taught me how to play a card game. I soon became an expert at it, and I played as adeptly with my toes as they did with their hands. When I'd win, Bill would throw back his head and laugh, while Bob would shake his head and say, "It's your fault, Bill. You taught her how to play. You can't blame me." But I knew he wasn't truly upset. His blue eyes always twinkled, and his lips twitched with a smile behind his steel gray mustache.

True to their word, my parents took me home most weekends. Now that I could be out of the iron lung for short periods of time, I always enjoyed the car ride. But best of all was getting home to play with Lena. I also loved when Ruth would read to me as I rested in my iron lung. I thought it was the coziest, happiest feeling of the day.

I wasn't read to only at home, though. The hospital's program for education was highly developed, and all the children who were old enough went to school every day for a few hours in the morning. I loved my schoolteacher. Miss Buck was from Germany, and she always made me smile.

Our day began with orderlies rolling the students on gurneys through the underground tunnel that connected our building with the Toomey Pavilion. "George?" I addressed the orderly in charge of me.

The orderly's dark face tipped politely. "Yes, Miz Vera?"

"Will the hot water from those pipes up there fall on my face?"

"Oh, not enough to hurt ya, child. Don't worry. I'll take good care of you." But I was still always afraid that water would fall on my face and make it hard for me to breathe. Sometimes a drop or two did land on me as we passed beneath the piping system. But this fear was always forgotten when we arrived at the schoolroom.

It was not set up with desks like a normal schoolroom. Instead, it had rows of beds. Miss Buck always met her students with a big smile. "Are we ready for the adventure of learning?"

"Yes!" my voice always held more enthusiasm than any of the other voices in the room.

"Today we are starting our first reader. You have all learned your phonics and now it's time to read!" She moved through the classroom with ease and imparted knowledge with humor and passion.

Some days we learned basic math facts or wrote letters to celebrities. Other days we read from our readers or had a science lesson. On more than one occasion Miss Buck brought in live animals for our classroom. The most memorable one of them all was Alec the baby alligator. He lived in a small tank on a shelf behind Miss Buck's desk.

One day Miss Buck announced that the local television station was coming to feature our school. "You are my best reading student, Vera," she told me. "Would you like to read for the cameramen?" I was thrilled. It was fun to be the center of attention and to perform a reading in my best voice.

After a visit home one weekend, I was anticipating our usual school routine as well as a visit with my friend Paul. But when I awoke Monday morning, I didn't see Paul in his iron lung. Puzzled, I asked the nearest nurse, "Where is Paul?"

For a moment she looked at me as if she didn't know what to say. "Did he move?" I asked. "Did he go home?"

"Well, honey . . . he went home in one way. Instead of going to sleep last night, Paul went to heaven instead."

"Oh, no!" I shook my head. "Paul died? I can't see him now!" I looked up into her face, crying.

"Shh, honey. There now. Don't cry. I know we'll miss Paul. But he's in a better place."

She put her arm around me soothingly and patted my head. I pulled away and looked up at her desperately. "Do you think he can run and play up there, Nurse?"

She smiled gently. "Oh, yes, Vera. I'm sure of it. He is happy now and he'll never be sick again. Just remember, goodbye is not forever."

"I know he wanted to run again," I said, blinking away tears. "Someday I'll see him again." Though my heart grieved for the loss of my friend, I knew in a solemn sort of way that he was happier now, and I accepted it without further question.

That night when I was tucked in I made sure the doll Paul had given me for my last birthday was snuggled in next to me. "Good night, Paul," I whispered. I had named my doll after him and now it was my only tangible reminder of him. I missed my friend every day. But I adjusted quickly as the young often do. I never feared death for myself or anyone else. It was just a fact to me that Paul had needed to go to heaven.

After Paul's passing, my visits home were even more of a highlight. I worked hard in school and enjoyed the afternoon visits from the social workers. The hospital staff worked hard to keep us entertained and brought in visitors ranging from "magicians" who could pull real rabbits from their hats, to people dressed up like celebrities. There were picnics and programs and projects. And now that I could go outside in a wheelchair, even Lena could come visit me sometimes. She was only four but she could push my wheelchair all by herself. I was proud of her!

During these busy days, other important things were happening in the polio world. The remarkable staff at Cleveland, including Dr. Fredrick C. Robbins and two other physicians, received the Nobel Prize in 1954 for successfully growing the polio virus in a tissue culture. They went on from there to engineer both the Salk (killed virus) and Sabin (live virus) vaccines.

In April of 1955 the whole United States celebrated wildly as a formal broadcast announced the field test results of the Salk vaccine. The tests on the vaccines had proven that they were almost completely effective in preventing paralytic polio. The disease that had changed my life forever had begun to be conquered at last!

In the fall of that year, after 999 days in the Aultman and Cleveland hospitals, I went home.

CHAPTER 6

WORLD OF WONDER

"Leon, put two chairs together. They'll be the beds," I directed. "Ruth, you can be the head nurse. You can be Mrs. Gaston." We were setting up a hospital in the big farm kitchen. Ever since I'd come home, my siblings had been fascinated by my stories about my days in the hospital. Today we had decided we were going to have our own play hospital.

"Will the shots hurt?" Lena asked pitifully. She was a patient and I had announced that all sick patients received shots.

I looked at her and we giggled. Then I put on my best sober air and instructed our doctor what to say. "Fred, since you're the doctor you have to tell your patients that the shots are good for them."

Fred chuckled a little abashedly. "Are they? Well, Lena, shots are good for you, so I guess you'll have to get one."

Lena giggled again and I shook my head impatiently. "No, Fred. Doctors aren't like that. You have to be very sober and comforting."

Ruth bustled about, making Lena, Leon, and JoAnn comfortable with couch pillows and afghans. I thought she was almost as good as a real nurse.

Little JoAnn looked scared of the shot when the good doctor Fred came to administer what I had ordered. She shook her head and her lower lip trembled. "Me not sick." She sat up and pushed the blanket away. Fred looked to me for guidance, and I decided that she could be given medicine on a spoon instead. She was much more content with this arrangement, and the day was saved.

When we were done with our play world, the kitchen was a mess of pans and water cups and blankets. But Mama never made a fuss about it. She simply made us clean it up. As long as we were happy and content, she was glad to let us imagine.

Life at home was orderly. Dad was very particular about the family schedule. Family worship was always a part of our day. My mornings were full of Mama doing my exercises with me, working my muscles in an endless effort to strengthen them. My arms were pitifully thin. My legs were stronger due to being used much more for my daily life. She made sure I took my vitamins to keep my strength up, and every day at lunch she or Ruth would put my braces on so I could sit up and use my hands to eat with the rest of the family.

Oh, how I hated those braces! One day I was especially vexed with the frustration of the bulky metal contraptions. Fortunately for me, Ruth was the one putting them on me. I took my strong little legs and kicked her shins. If it had been Mama I would have simply had to comply, but somehow it felt relieving to fight the things I hated so much.

"Ouch, Vera. Stop. I'm trying to help you!" Ruth protested.

"Just stop. I don't want to wear them. They hurt," I shot back.

"No. Mama said you were going to wear them." Ruth wrestled the corset on me, and I pouted.

Kick! Kick!

"Oww . . . stop this minute, Vera, or I'll kick you back," Ruth puffed.

"You can't boss me. I won't wear them," I insisted stubbornly.

We exchanged two or three more kicks before Ruth's strength won over my persistence. Later when Mama asked why my shins were bruised I told her Ruth had done it. When Mama asked her about it, she protested that I had started it, and she'd only kicked back in self defense. Mama almost didn't believe her since her shins didn't have any bruises. She warned us both to behave and help each other instead of fighting in the future. When she left the room, Ruth looked at me sheepishly, and I broke into a grin.

"Sorry. But I still hate those braces."

"Sorry too. I shouldn't have kicked you. But you shouldn't fight me. Mom almost didn't believe me. It's really not fair, Vera." She couldn't help chuckling in spite of herself. We both dissolved into laughter and our conflict was forgotten—until it was time to wear them again the next day.

Despite our fights over the braces, Ruth was one of my best friends during those early months and years at home. Mama rarely let me go out in those early months since I was susceptible to colds, and any illness connected with breathing could easily turn into a crisis for me with my limited lung capacity.

When Mama and Dad were both gone in the evenings to church meetings, Ruth would put the other children to bed upstairs and then pull my iron lung into the kitchen. There she would fry bologna for a snack, and then while I talked to her, we would design doll dress patterns that she would use to sew mini doll garments. Often she'd sit next to me by the hour and read to me.

When I entered the second grade, Miss Delilah Miller started teaching me in our home every afternoon after her normal school day was finished. I loved my teacher. Just like Miss Buck at Cleveland, Sister Delilah loved learning and opened up worlds of wonderful things to me through her enthusiastic teaching and gentle, observant coaching.

"Here, Vera. Let's try again." She wrapped my fingers gently around the pencil and guided my hand. Although my arms and most of the muscles in my hand were useless, I could move a few of my fingers a bit. I had learned to print from Miss Buck, but now Sister Delilah was teaching me the cursive alphabet. I concentrated hard, giving all my effort to the lovely script in front of me.

"There, that's how you do it. Yes, just like that. Now you try." Her smile encouraged me. Smiling back, I grasped the pencil and slowly, painstakingly, tried again.

We talked about grammar and math some days, but my favorite days were spent talking about books and history and geography. I loved social studies and voraciously read whatever story books my teacher gave me to study.

During this year of second grade, another sister joined our family. She was born on New Year's Day, and my parents named her Delilah after my much-loved teacher. I loved my little sister intensely right from the start. Using my legs, I'd lie on the sofa and hold her between my knees, just as if they were arms. Mama let me hold her often. Sometimes she would lie on my bed in my room with me while I rested during the day. I liked to watch her soft little mouth move and blow bubbles, and when she fussed I'd stick my toes in her mouth to pacify her. They were clean toes. I just used them instead of my fingers, and my baby sister didn't mind at all.

Though my life was filled with wonderful things, sometimes there were boring stretches when all my older siblings were away and my little siblings were sleeping or doing chores. My hospital bed was set up in Grandma's old room on the main floor. It sat right by a window overlooking the road. I thought it would be interesting if a wreck or something happened on the road. But most of the time I contented myself with imagining what I would be someday when I grew up, or dreaming up the next game to play with my siblings when they were free. I also spent a lot of time reading various books. Books were my best friends in those long, quiet hours.

As winter went on and gave way to spring, my classmates would sometimes come with my teacher during recess time to spend an hour with me. Sitting under the warm sun on a blanket, we'd read stories and laugh. I kept up with my studies and got very good grades.

One of my favorite pastimes outside of school and family life was spending time with my pets and stretching my horizons. Dad built me a four-wheeled walker so I could get around the house by myself. In my eight-year-old mind it needed a romantic title, so I called it my "Freedom Maker." I had a vibrant green parakeet that sat on the rail of my walker and whistled and trilled to me whenever I didn't pay enough attention to him. I liked to talk to him about how I felt about life.

My other animal friend was my adored terrier. His silky fur and chocolate brown eyes made me think he was the most beautiful creature in the world. He was mischievous at times, but he always looked out for my wellbeing and seemed to know exactly how I was feeling. Some days when I was lonely or disappointed about something, my little dog would climb up on my bed and stick his nose under my arm. We'd watch the rain splash on the window above my bed, and I'd whisper my woes to him. He never told my secrets, and when I was happy again he'd wag his tail and bark a little as if to say, "I told you it wasn't so bad." Then I'd giggle and all would be well.

My times of feeling lonely or bored were truly rare. Almost always someone was there to play with me or help pass the time. Lena was especially near and always involved me in all she did. We became almost inseparable. If Lena did something while I watched, she'd always tell the story later as if we had done it together. And of course we had. I was simply doing it in my heart while she acted it out.

Some moments with my siblings were wild ones. Like the day Mama sent us to a store just down the road for thread. Fred was pushing me in my wheelchair. There was a steep little hill we had to go down to get to our destination, and at the top Fred decided I would enjoy an adventure. Without a thought as to what danger might be involved, he let go of my wheelchair. He ran alongside as we gained momentum. Faster and faster it seemed to go. I felt the warm summer wind whooshing through my hair, and Fred had all he could do to keep the chair from tipping over as he ran alongside. When we reached the bottom of the hill, I felt breathless and realized I'd been screaming the whole way down.

Flushed and breathing hard, Fred grinned at me and I grinned back. "That was fun. It almost felt like I was running," I laughed.

On another day I decided that I'd like to try riding our brown pony. My siblings involved me in everything without question. I was just one of them. "Easy," said Fred as he guided the horse into a safe position next to me. Lena lifted me up so I could get on. Holding the reins with one hand, Fred took my small body in his other arm, and with my legs slung over the saddle I gripped hard with my knees.

"Okay, ready?" he asked cheerfully.

"Yes. Let's go," I said excitedly. It felt wonderful to try things like this and realize the exhilaration of accomplishing them.

With a touch of his feet Fred set the pony in motion, and we cantered out the farm lane.

"Can we gallop?" I asked. "I love the feel of the wind in my hair."

I felt Fred nod and heard him cluck to the pony. Its head went down and its pace quickened. Soon we were in a full-out gallop with gravel spraying behind us. I was too breathless to laugh, but my heart was bursting with joy. Wind swept past my face and the warm summer smells rushed up to meet us from the passing ditches.

When we pulled up in front of the barn again, I laughed. "It felt like flying, didn't it, Fred?"

He grinned down at me and nodded. "Sure, Vera. I'm glad you liked it." I always felt safe with Fred.

I hardly even realized my limitations most of the time. If I wanted to try something, I told someone what to do and how to help me, and I almost always accomplished my goal.

One day I told Lena I wanted to climb the silo. She didn't ask questions. "Okay. Let's." She and I made our way through the dusty barnyard to the towering round silo. Squinting up at the hot afternoon sun, I waited for Lena to grasp my shoulders and lift me as she always did. Then I used my feet to climb the rungs. "It's fun," I puffed.

Lena laughed behind me, puffing and pushing. "When we get to the top, I wonder what we'll see."

We wrestled up six rungs of the narrow ladder before we realized we were stuck. "It's too hard, Lena. We have to get down."

"How am I supposed to get you down?" she asked matter-of-factly. "We can't turn around."

"Well, call for help then," I told her, beginning to feel desperate.

"Help!" She called loudly. Thankfully Fred was in the barn and came running at our call.

"What are you girls doing?" he called anxiously.

"Just climbing up. But we can't get down," Lena explained.

He helped us down without scolding us, but I could tell he thought the idea had been a bit foolish. It wasn't the last crazy plan we tried, but other times we enjoyed more success.

When I went back to Cleveland for checkups and brace adjustments, Lena often went along. Sometimes a specialist would tell me proudly that I was progressing wonderfully and could graduate from a particular brace. I used some of them regularly, but other braces they sent home with me sat almost untouched. It was when I graduated from these unused braces "with success" that Lena and I always laughed together after the specialist left the room.

"You didn't even use that one, and they think it fixed you," Lena would giggle behind her hand.

"Shh. It's our secret," I would giggle back.

If they prescribed a new brace in the unused brace's place, we'd exchange knowing glances and giggle some more. Sometimes Mama looked at us and wondered what we thought was so funny. We only shook our heads and said, "Oh, just a little game we like to play together." And she'd smile and wisely desist from any further questions.

CHAPTER 7

OF STARS AND SNOWBALLS

The sleigh runners whispered over the thin crust of snow. The pony's hooves crunched lightly in the still night air, throwing up a fine spray of snow as his trot ate up the pasture ground. I sat warmly bundled in the sleigh bed on top of the straw, my head tipped back. Above us the velvety night sky stretched, singing silent wonder with its spread of sparkling constellations and planets.

"See, there's the Big Dipper," Lena pointed out, waving a mittened hand.

"And there's the Seven Sisters constellation." I squinted to see the muted star group amidst its brighter neighbors.

"Kind of like us. Except we need another girl to make us seven yet," Lena observed.

Judy had joined the family in midsummer of last year, right after our big move to a new farm in Suffield, Ohio. That made eight children in all, and the noise and joy in our household mushroomed. Dad had built us the sleigh to use behind our brown pony. It was a heavy wooden box with skids. Since it was

Friday night and we had no school the next morning, Fred had offered to take Lena and me for a ride. He was on the pony's back, since the pony drove best this way. It had taken Dad a lot of time and energy to break our tough little horse, but once he'd been harnessed and settled down, he made a wonderful working pet for us children to enjoy.

I loved the outdoors. There was something about the vast beauty of nature that always made me feel closer to God outside than anywhere else. Tonight as I looked up at the stars, I wondered if anything could be more enjoyable than sleighing under a winter night sky.

Fred guided the pony in a wide circle and headed back toward the house. The whisper of runners sped up as the pony lengthened his stride. He knew we were headed toward his warm stall and hay to munch. Snow flew up from his hooves and fell on the blanket in our laps in clumps now. One small clod landed on my hood and made me laugh at a sudden memory.

"Lena, remember that time last winter when Dad was taking me to school? The snowball story?"

Lena giggled. "I sure do. Dad was so upset! I wish I would have been there to see it."

It had been like any other day. Dad drove me to school at 1:00 every afternoon for my two hours of classes in Sister Anna's third grade classroom. It was snowing hard—the wet kind of snow that sticks to everything and is perfect for snowballs but miserable to drive in.

As we pulled into the parking lot, Dad rolled down his window to scrape snow off his mirror. Without warning, a well-packed snowball came hurtling through the window. It hit Dad hard in the side of the head and sent his hat flying, scattering snow all over me where I sat beside him.

Without a second thought, Dad was out of the truck and slamming the door behind him. When the students saw him coming, they scattered—but Dad was fast. I saw him through the open window. Three long strides and he had the culprit in his grip. I heard his strong voice scolding, "Don't you ever do that again! I don't like having my face hit with a snowball while I'm driving. And you hit Vera too!"

I winced and giggled at the same time as he washed the boy's face thoroughly in the wet snow before he let him go. Red-faced and thoroughly chastened for his thoughtlessness, the boy ducked away and ran for the schoolhouse. The word traveled through the school that week, "Don't mess with Vera's dad." But despite Dad's stern personality, I never felt afraid of him. To me he was my safe and strong protector.

I loved school in third grade as much as I had loved it in first grade at Cleveland. I had a bed in the back of the classroom where I could lie and study. With leggings under my dress, I used my foot as a hand and raised it when I wanted to say something or ask a question. I used my toes to write and keep my books in neatly stacked order. And I used them to turn the pages when it was time to study.

One of my favorite parts of school was getting to know the other girls my age. My budding friendship with Karen Wagler in particular was a great source of joy for me. I loved socializing, but I also enjoyed my studies. I excelled at English and history, and math came easily to me. However, science always kept me studying hard to keep up with the other students. The one part of science I did love was medical science. If I had the chance, I would devour whole books on the medical world and medical science. Having been in the hospital so long as a young child gave me an enduring fascination with and appreciation for the study of disease and its treatment and how the body functions.

At the end of every school day, Ruth would help me put on my full-body brace for the short ride home on the bus. We lived just a half mile from the school. Here I did not fight her about the braces as I sometimes did at home. I knew they were the price of my freedom, and I was grateful for her help.

Despite my two hours a day at school, I still had plenty of time on my hands to imagine activities to pass the time. More and more now, Lena was my constant playmate. Dad and Mama had decided somewhere in all our fights about the braces that it wasn't necessary for me to sit at the table to eat supper. Instead, Lena was allowed to join me in the living room where we dined in our own make-believe world, me lying on the sofa and Lena sitting cross-legged on the floor beside me, her plate in her lap.

Often our conversations involved our make-believe husbands. "Richard, I was going to ask you earlier today about Tommy's troubles in school, but I forgot," I would begin, addressing a question to my husband. "Perhaps Lena and Dale will have some advice for us."

Lena would look very wise and cock her head to one side while her husband Dale spoke. Then shaking her head a little, she'd say, "Well, I think he'll probably grow out of it. He's such a bright child for his age. Perhaps he gets bored easily compared to normal children because of how quickly he learns. Don't worry too much, Vera. Our daughter Stacy was almost the same way at Tommy's age."

We discussed nearly everything a grownup world could hold in our evening conversations among the "four" of us. We had chummy times, only occasionally being distracted by our make-believe children, since they were usually very busy playing with each other.

Other afternoons, especially when the weather was very cold, we played "good nurse/bad nurse," which was a game of my creating. I would "act out" what a good nurse was like for my little siblings. But they always liked it best when I acted out the bad nurse. "There, I am turning my patient over roughly," I would announce.

"May I have salt for these potatoes, please?"

"Oh, no! Salt is not good for you. No salt for those potatoes. Eat them quickly now!"

"But, Nurse, I am thirsty. May I have a drink?"

"Not till you've finished your food, child. Eat!" My little siblings would giggle at this impersonation, and I enjoyed the imagining as much as they did.

When summer came again, Lena and I expanded our exploration. We would often meander back to the pasture and sit in the grass and dream together. One day we'd find a robin's nest, or another day it would be a rabbit hiding in the long grass.

One day as we meandered back along the cow paths, Lena suddenly looked behind us and squealed. "Vera! Vera, hurry! There's a cow coming fast and she looks angry!" I didn't have time to look back before Lena had taken me in her wiry little arms and half-thrown me under the fence. I gasped for breath and Lena came slithering breathlessly after me on her stomach.

She sat up and helped me sit up, her face red and her eyes frightened. We both looked back and saw the cow watching us from a few feet away, her large, dark eyes full of curiosity, but not hate. "Oh, Lena, you scared me so much! What made you think she was angry?"

Lena brushed stray hair from her face and grinned. "She was trotting toward us. Cows don't usually run unless they're upset, do they?"

"I don't know, but at least she doesn't look upset now. Let's go get a drink. It's hot out here."

On another day we decided to climb the grain elevator. Our previous attempt at climbing the silo had been unsuccessful, but the grain elevator seemed more reasonable. In truth it was more dangerous than climbing the silo. We'd been reading about mountain climbing just the day before, and our active imaginations saw the grain elevator as a perfect substitute. With our usual vim and vigor, we climbed to the top. Lena was behind me, lifting up my shoulders so that I could step to the next slat. Finally we were high enough that we could look out over the farmyard.

"But how are we going to get down?" Lena asked suddenly.

"I don't know. But look at the view, Lena. Isn't it amazing?"

"Yes . . . but I don't know how I'm going to get you down," Lena repeated. She seemed to feel quite worried, and I looked at our situation with a critical eye.

"You have to get around me so I can go in front of you," I said matter-of-factly. "And I'll need to turn around to go down so I can see where my feet are."

"Okay, you lie down and I'll step over you. Otherwise one of us might fall," she instructed. She laid me down on the slats. The earth was dizzyingly far below us. After she was above me, she slowly turned me around so that my back was against the slats. Then she wedged her body between my back and the slats until she could put one arm under my arms and lock it into position over my chest. Holding me securely in this way, she helped to guide my feet downward.

Tediously and cautiously, we maneuvered our way back down, slat by slat, until we reached the barnyard below. Lena sighed when we were safely down. "That was fun. But I was pretty scared," she admitted, grinning sheepishly.

Another summer delight was the pond Dad dug for us with a rented backhoe. He built it large enough for all of us to swim in during the summer and skate on in the winter. On hot August afternoons after the garden work and housework were finished, all of us children would troop down through the pasture and immerse ourselves in the cool depths.

There was a rubber raft for me, since I couldn't swim. They tied it to the dock, and I would paddle it around with my legs. I loved the feel of the hot sun on my face and arms while the cool water lapped over my dusty toes. It was one of my favorite summer activities besides picnics in the field with Dad and the boys.

When Dad was harvesting the wheat or making hay, Mama often announced a picnic. Ruth and Lena would help her pack everything neatly in a basket, and we'd all go out to the field where Dad was working with Fred and Leon. I loved to sit on the big quilt in the sun with my family and eat and talk and laugh together. It always made me think of Laura Ingalls Wilder and the stories she told of helping Pa harvest.

Fourth grade started that fall of 1958, and my parents decided that I was physically strong enough to attend school full time with my other siblings. The first day of school, excitement ran high. Karen met me in the hall, her eyes glowing. "Vera, I get to sit by you when you sit at your desk during devotions."

I smiled back at her. I was excited to be more a part of school than ever. But I couldn't be in my braces for long. After Sister Marian finished leading devotions that first morning, Karen went with me to the library and helped me take off my brace.

Over lunch that day, we caught up on our summer and talked about our dreams of the future. "What do you want to be someday, Karen?"

"I think I'll be a stewardess," Karen stated brightly. With her vivacious personality, she always had a lot of friends.

"Oh, that would suit you really well," I exclaimed, smiling.

"What about you?" Karen asked, blushing a little.

"I want to be a secretary. I like keeping things in order," I confided.

I could write with my hands now, but I still studied on a bed in the back of the schoolroom and used my foot as a hand when I needed to raise it to get the teacher's attention.

My classmates involved me in their games, and I became a natural leader among them. I rarely thought of my handicap at all when I lived such a full life. Only when I had to put my braces back on for the ride home, or when I couldn't run to take part in a softball game, did I feel a bit of sadness about being limited.

But I did not allow others to bully those who had physical limitations. One day at school I overheard some older boys making fun of another student who occasionally had epileptic seizures. The boy's face was a picture of embarrassed misery. He hung his head and looked sheepish and hurt as the other boys laughed. Everything in me rose up to his defense, and I marched over to those boys and looked the ringleader right in the eye. Glaring, I shook my head as if I were his mother. "If you don't stop making fun of him right now, I will tell the teacher," I declared vehemently.

Shocked, the boys looked at me with their mouths open and their eyes wide. "Well, okay then," the ringleader sputtered. They melted away, and the boy whom they'd been mocking gave me a quick glance before he followed. I saw gratitude in his eyes and I smiled at him, suddenly feeling shy. I never saw them make fun of him again.

A favorite pastime we siblings enjoyed during our grade-school summers was a club called Silo Hill Club. At our weekly meetings, I presided as head of the club.

"We will start with reading the rules as usual. Remember that the purpose of our club is to encourage good behavior and discourage bad behavior."

Everyone would nod solemnly and I would continue. "The rules are as follows: 1. No talking back to parents. 2. No fighting with brothers and sisters. 3. No being mean to pets. 4. Clean up your room."

Then from oldest to youngest we'd confess which rules we'd broken that week. The fine for each broken rule was one penny, and we kept them all in a little jar. Fred never seemed to break any of the rules. But Lena, Leon, and I almost always contributed a penny to the penalty jar. By the time we had parted with our pennies, we were always ready for the cheerful appearance of our oldest sister Ruth, with refreshments she often contributed to our meetings. Our club would break up with laughter and glib advice on how to do better in the week to come.

CHAPTER 8

AWAKENINGS

"It's so much fun at your house," Karen sighed.

I grinned. "Well, I think it's fun at your house where it's totally quiet and we can do whatever we want."

"Yeah, sometimes I wish Mom were home more often, though," she confided. She yawned and stretched out on the bed. I could see she was preparing for one of our late night conversations. Saturday night sleepovers were a normal part of our friendship, and the camaraderie that had been born back in the early grades of school had only grown through the years. Now in the sixth grade, it was taking on a new dimension as we awakened to the world around us in new ways.

"What do you think makes our house so fun?" I asked curiously.

"Well, you always have someone to talk to, for one thing. Your family meal times are like a class discussion on world events mixed with a comedy play of ten different actors."

I giggled. "We do talk about everything together," I agreed.

"And fight." Karen shook her head in mock disgust. In another second she turned sober. "But your parents just seem so . . ." she paused as if searching for words. "Involved, I guess. I mean, you all kiss your mom and dad good night every night. A lot of families don't have that kind of love. And your dad is always planning new fun for you and your brothers and sisters."

I looked at my best friend thoughtfully. She had a good family, but she was the youngest and the rest of her siblings were in college. Her mom had gone back to school as well, and Karen spent a lot of time alone.

"I still say I like your quiet house sometimes, but anytime you are lonely you know you can come stay with us," I assured her staunchly. "I guess I just think our family is normal. I never thought about how much fun we really do have together."

"Speaking of fun together, have you thought any more about our Girls Everlasting Club?" Karen inquired. "I've had so many ideas since we talked about it on Thursday."

"I think I like the idea," I responded readily. "Lena wants to be in on it too."

"Okay. Well, I think we should plan out our first meeting at least. Then next week we'll be ready to start. I was thinking we could go sing for my grandma. And maybe for our neighbor lady. She has cancer, and I think it would cheer her up if we would visit her."

"So basically we want to do good deeds and cheer people up."

"Yes. Do you want to be vice president and Lena can be the secretary?"

"That's a good idea. There comes Lena now. Let's ask her."

Lena readily agreed to our new plans, and the club was launched in the following weeks. We made potholders and visited various older ladies to sing for them. When we visited Karen's neighbor, I held back a little. Her nose was half eaten away from her cancer and her looks scared me, but she seemed very happy that we had come to see her.

Besides our club, winter activities and parties filled the cold months with fun. When the ice froze over long enough, Dad always took a rod out and measured it for thickness. We would wait eagerly for him to return to the house and declare that it was "safe for skating." Then we'd plan the first skating party of the year. It was always a grand occasion. My siblings and their friends would all troop down and put on their skates in the warming house, where Fred would have built a small fire in the little stove in preparation for the event.

Mom and I would drive out in the truck to sit and watch. In the beam of the headlights, everyone would put on a skating show for us. Lena would make a fast loop and then Fred would zoom through a figure eight after her, followed by jumps and spins and curves from all the other gliding skaters. We let them know how pleased we were with a particular performance by flashing the lights off and on.

Toboggan riding was another merry winter highlight. Fred carried me up the hill in his strong arms. It was a steep hill, and I couldn't wait to feel the swish of the speeding sled beneath us. We had a piece of corrugated tin to use that Fred had designed with a makeshift brake of sorts.

"Ready?" He grinned at me and I laughed.

"Sure!"

The hill streamed past in a breakneck speeding spray of powdery snow, and the cold whipped my face until wind tears rolled down my cheeks. It was over faster than it started. At the bottom, Fred ground the brake hard to stop us before we hit the fence.

"Oh, Fred, that was delightful!"

He grinned. "Want to go again?"

And then there was ice fishing on Berlin Lake. Dad would take Lena, Leon, and me out to sit in the ice shanty with him on a Saturday afternoon.

"Shh . . . if you aren't quiet the fish won't bite," Leon would plead.

Lena and I would concentrate on silence for several moments. Then Lena would get bored and grin at me. I'd grin back and pretty soon we were giggling and talking. It didn't take much to set us off. But we still caught fish.

"It's a bluegill!" I would exclaim, pulling it up through the ice hole and holding it out for my brother to take off the hook.

"Now that makes three bass and four bluegills. If we can catch a couple more of each before Dad's done with those burgers, we'll have enough for Mom to fry for supper tonight," Leon would calculate.

Dad would just listen with a quiet smile on his face, half hidden in blue smoke as he fried burgers and bacon on the little wood-burning stove he'd created for the shanty.

When they were finished, we'd bite into their juicy deliciousness and sigh with sheer delight. "Mmm . . . so good."

When we got back to the house with the fish, Dad cleaned them. With Ruth's faithful help, Mom dipped each fillet in cornmeal and spices and fried them golden brown.

"JoAnn and Delilah, time to set the table," Mom would call the little girls. I held baby David to keep him happy during the meal preparations. He'd joined our family the previous year and was loved and doted on by all of his older sisters.

When we all thought we could bear the tantalizing odors no longer, Mom would call us and we'd sit around the long table. The clock told us it was the usual precise supper time: 6:00. Our grumbling stomachs were more impatient than usual when we saw the layers of steaming fish stacked around a heaping mound of crisp, hot French fries on Mom's special green platter.

After prayer, the normal conversations would ensue. "Did you hear the latest news on the presidential candidates?" Dad asked. Now that some of us were older, we took a bit more interest in the outside world.

"Do you think John F. Kennedy will win the elections?" Fred asked.

After speculating over the present predictions that the end times were near, we discussed the race between the Soviet Union and the United States to put a man on the moon.

"I wonder what it's like on the moon?" Lena and I said together. We often shared the same thoughts.

"Do you think there are people on the moon?" Delilah asked.

"No, Lilah, of course not. That's silly," JoAnn corrected.

"No it's not," I defended my little sister. "I used to wonder the same things sometimes."

"Well, I think it's cold on the moon," Lena suggested.

"I wish I could go to the moon. Wouldn't that be amazing? It would be like being in a whole new world!" I dreamed.

"They say it can't be done," Ruth stated practically.

"Scientists have already accomplished things we thought were impossible. You never know what they might accomplish, given enough time," Dad smiled.

Mom passed the platter for a third time and soon not a single French fry or fish fillet remained. We all pushed back from the table with sighs of contentment and thanked our mother for the delicious supper.

I usually attended church, but not always through grade school. Mostly I just couldn't sit for that length of time. Lena and I would go out to the car together and wait for the rest of the family. Sometimes one of the church mothers let us care for a fussy baby in our car so she could enjoy the service without distraction.

I grew up steadily hearing the truths of Scripture with Mom reading Bible stories, Dad leading us in devotions, hymns being sung in school, and bits and pieces of sermons playing through my head. But as I grew older, I became increasingly aware that there was something I didn't yet have.

I had always had a simple faith in God, just like I had in my earthly father. I viewed God as someone kind and protective but perhaps a bit distant. My first distinct memory of personal impressions of God was on a visit home from the hospital. I had been sitting out on the back porch by the trailing honeysuckle. It had just rained, and the fresh smell of clean earth and honeysuckle flowed over me gently. With sudden clarity, I wondered if there was any more perfect smell than this refreshing, newly-washed clean air. And I knew that God must be perfect too, because He had created the smell.

Now He was stirring my heart with a yearning to know that perfection personally. In the fall of 1960, an evangelist named Myron Augsburger came to Hartville to conduct tent meetings. The whole family attended, and although I couldn't sit through the service in the tent, Dad found a way to park the car close enough to the tent so that I could hear the sermon through the open car window.

The end of the week came without anything really significant standing out to me. But on one of the last nights I saw my Dad making his way toward the car with his arm around Fred's shoulders. Startled, I wondered what had taken place. Dad rarely displayed affection for his children in public.

Mom got to the car first. As she got in with David in her lap, I asked her, "Why is Dad hugging Fred? Did he do something?"

Mom's gentle face lit up with a smile as she looked back at me with tears in her eyes. "Fred surrendered his life to Christ tonight, Vera."

"Oh . . . that's wonderful. But, Mom, what does that mean?" I suddenly realized I didn't know just what people meant when they said that.

"Vera." There was quiet reproof in her tone. "You should listen to the sermons better. Fred's personal decision to follow Christ tonight means that he gave his life to God. When the altar call was given, Fred asked someone to pray with him. He has promised to follow God with his life no matter what the cost."

Lena got into the car beside me, and Dad and Fred reached the vehicle at nearly the same time. I looked carefully at my older brother, studying his face. He looked somehow stronger, and a quiet happiness rested on his face.

Later in bed, Lena and I discussed the matter. By this time, I had graduated from the iron lung to a chest respirator that allowed me to sleep in a regular bed. "Lena, did you hear what happened to Fred?"

"Of course." Lena sounded sleepy.

"Well, haven't we given our lives to Jesus too? I mean we pray and apologize and make it right when we sin."

"I think so."

"Lena, I'm serious. I really wish I knew more. Somehow what happened tonight feels different from anything I've really thought about before now."

"Sometimes I ask the same questions." Lena's voice was thoughtful.

"Can I sleep with you?" A little voice at the foot of our bed interrupted our conversation.

"JoAnn, what are you doing?" Lena asked.

"I want to sleep with you. Please?"

"Don't look at her," I whispered. "She'll go away if you ignore her."

Lena had a softer heart than I did when it came to such things.

"We can let her sleep at the foot of the bed."

"Fine," I sighed. "She's really not behaving by coming in here, but I guess it won't hurt."

"You can sleep at our feet," Lena said aloud.

Our six-year-old sister fairly bounced up on the bed with happiness. Lying down and making herself as small as possible, she giggled. "Good night, Vera. Good night, Lena."

"You have to be quiet if you sleep with us," I instructed firmly.

"Okay." With another giggle, she closed her eyes tight and pretended to be asleep while we went back to our conversation.

A year would go by before my searching questions would be answered. During revival meetings in seventh grade, my best friend Karen made her decision for Christ.

The following day I realized it was time for me to make a decision as well—a public decision to follow Christ. While the congregation sang "Just as I Am," I rose to my feet with a wildly beating heart. My hands were sweaty and I trembled inside, but I was determined to go forward.

"Help me do this, Lord," I breathed quietly. Tears streamed down my face as I made my way to the front of the sanctuary.

A lady from church named Magdalena Detweiler prayed with me in a back room. It was a moment of decision that would change my whole life. "Lord, I am coming just as I am, and I want to be yours forever," I prayed simply. "Wash me and cleanse me from my sin. Jesus, thank you for dying for my sin. Please come in and make me new, like you. I give my life to you."

As the women of the church hugged me with joy and welcomed me into the family of God, my heart sang. I felt so clean and alive! Just like the fragrant and perfect smell of a rain-washed world.

CHAPTER 9

THY ROD AND STAFF COMFORT ME

The hot summer air brushed our faces as we sped faster and faster. The bike picked up speed down yet another hill. "Hold on!" Lena yelled. My little dog barked sharply in his basket between the handlebars, his ears whipping back in the wind. I sat astride my pillow sidesaddle and gripped the bike bar tighter with my bare toes. My foot was only an inch from the bike chain, but I didn't think of the danger. This was the way to ride!

Lena and I had worked hard for this red Schwinn boys' bike we both loved. It had come from our egg money. Those thirty dollars came from good, honest sweat.

Dad had bought thirty laying hens, and he allowed us to keep the money from the eggs if we were willing to clean them. Lena always did the work. But in our usual way, I kept her constant company as if I were doing it along with her.

I had to smile now at the numerous memories of those hours watching my lithe sister work industriously, her brown eyes glancing up to laugh into mine every little while. When she picked up a particularly dirty egg, I would exclaim, "Ew. Smash it, Lena!" With one quick flick, the egg would be smeared against the wall. Laughter would echo and Lena would wash her fingers before reaching for another egg. This went on until Mom heard about it. After her forbidding the waste of good eggs, we made up for the smashing habit with vehement "Eww . . . gross!" exclamations instead.

Our bike wasn't the only thing we drove. One day when Dad and Mom were gone, Lena and I had an hour to spare and decided to try something new. Our old, black, stick shift truck was parked in the driveway in its usual place. With both excitement and trepidation, Lena and I climbed in.

"How are we going to manage this?" Lena giggled.

"I'll tell you how," I assured her. "I'll push on the accelerator and you can do the rest. That way we can say I drove the truck and everyone will wonder how we ever managed such a thing," I grinned.

As I entered adolescence, I had grown more aware of my limitations. But I wasn't about to stop trying whatever came to mind. When I had leisure hours of rest, I'd work out in my mind just how we could accomplish the goals we talked about late at night under our covers.

"Okay, Lena. I'll sit here and use my good leg on the accelerator." I was almost lying down and could barely peer out the window from my position, but I could reach and control the speed of the truck.

Lena turned the ignition and the engine rumbled to life. Taking the wheel in both hands, she looked at me and grinned. "We're crazy."

"I know. Ready? Go. Let out the clutch."

With a lurch, she let out the clutch and ground the gears. The truck lurched forward and died, coasting to a stop.

"Try again," I cheered.

After an hour of practice, we puttered out the driveway with Lena instructing me when to push harder and when to let up on the gas pedal. "Now faster."

We turned left on the road and sped up until we reached the second driveway. Here we turned again and roared back up into our yard. When we had made several rounds, we were both exhausted from the effort. I grinned at Lena triumphantly. "We did it."

She chuckled. "We did. We can now officially say we know how to drive."

My brothers included me in their pursuits as well. When Fred told a hunting story one evening at supper, it occurred to me that I had never shot a gun. When he'd finished his story, I looked up from my meal and asked, "Do you think I could shoot, Fred?"

He looked thoughtful for a moment before answering, "Well, I guess I don't see why not." So the next afternoon we went out to the field together. Balancing the gun on a fence post, he directed me on how and when to pull the trigger. The loud noise echoed in the hills around us and hurt my ears. But I'd accomplished one more thing I wasn't supposed to be able to do. It left a certain warm glow inside, a feeling that partly made up for the wrestling to accept my limitations.

My family never treated me as different. I noticed it more in public when others stared at me, asked questions, or pitied me. The braces I used to walk worked well, but when I walked to the front of the church I had to pull a lever to make them bend. It always clicked and I felt humiliated by this noise that drew undue attention to me.

To compensate for this, I became fastidiously aware of how I looked and what I wore. I also became more aware of the boys around me. *What do they think of me?* I wondered. I liked certain ones and not others—just like the other girls my age. Most of my fellow students and friends were very understanding and treated me as one of them. However, they also looked out for me.

One day in the halls at school, I tripped over a fellow student's broom. Without the use of my hands, I was helpless to catch myself. My fall could have been a disaster, but my quick-thinking fellow student caught me in his arms before I hit the floor.

Utterly embarrassed, my face grew hot and my quick tongue uttered the first words that came to mind. "Oh, forevermore!"

He grinned good-naturedly and saved the day with a quick, "Oh, no. Not forever—just for now."

When my baby brother Michael was born, we were all grateful he survived. The birth was full of complications, and it wasn't long before we realized

Michael had developmental damage to his brain due to the trauma at birth. Dad especially struggled with the situation. He had long ago learned to accept the will of God, but the cerebral palsy in this situation had been caused by a slightly inebriated delivery doctor who mishandled the birth forceps. How could this be the will of God?

One morning in family worship, Dad read Hebrews 12 to us. When he came to verses 5–8, he paused after each verse as if searching for deeper meaning:

> "And ye have forgotten the exhortation which speaketh unto you as unto children, My son, despise not thou the chastening of the Lord, nor faint when thou art rebuked of him: for whom the Lord loveth he chasteneth, and scourgeth every son whom he receiveth. If ye endure chastening, God dealeth with you as with sons; for what son is he whom the father chasteneth not? But if ye be without chastisement, whereof all are partakers, then are ye bastards, and not sons."

He was thoughtful as he looked around the room. "His rod and His staff are part of the way our Father brings comfort to our lives, children. We need to remember that, whatever we face. We need to trust His wisdom even when we don't understand and allow His discipline to teach us what He desires us to know."

We all loved Michael even more because of his handicap. But each of us had to wrestle through the bitterness of the experience, especially we older ones who understood. My dad's strong protective instinct made him vocalize his hurt. Mom never said much, but I saw the pain in her tender eyes when she looked at Michael sometimes. It wouldn't be very long, however, before we adapted to his condition the same as we'd adapted to mine. In time it would be completely normal to us to have this newest dimension to our family dynamics.

As I thought through my own realizations of what life might hold for me and how my limitations would affect me, it was Fred who helped most. Sometimes during the night I woke up and lay thinking, longing for a body that would function with ease. I didn't speak of it, but my curved spine and atrophied muscles caused constant pain, especially since I insisted on living such an active life. As I wrestled with God, I wondered what the answers were.

Around this time, Fred introduced me to Joni Eareckson Tada's story. I devoured her book *Joni*. I held my breath when she hit the bottom of the lake on a hot July day and broke her neck. I cried with her when she realized she would never walk again. I cheered for her when she chose victory over defeat even when that meant life in a wheelchair. Above all, I took her message to heart.

I was not a victim of chance. God had a plan for my life, and I was called to overcome the odds with grace and humor. I wanted to do this well. Triumph could come out of tragedy when a person chose to respond with an overcoming, cheerful spirit. And Joni didn't live life like a hermit. She lived a life helping and inspiring others. I purposed to do the same, and Joni became my living hero and example for years to come. I hoped that someday I could meet this amazing woman.

The year I was sixteen, I got a taste of reaching beyond my limitations into the lives of others. A series of fifty-one tornadoes in one day had devastated homes in Iowa, Indiana, Michigan, and Ohio. Two hundred sixty people were killed and thousands were left without homes. Our youth group was part of a group of young people who went to give aid. When Ruth decided to go, she looked at me and announced, "You are sixteen, Vera. You are going with us."

"Ruth, I can't pick up debris. I won't be able to help. What are you thinking?"

She shook her head firmly. "There are other ways to help, Vera. You'll see."

I agreed reluctantly. I was surprised in the days that followed to find that a listening ear and compassion were just as important as physical labor in the aftermath of the tragedy. I came away with a deepened understanding of what it meant to live for others and not to limit God in how He uses our lives.

Other impacting influences during this stage of my life included Alvin Coblentz, who was principal of the Hartville Christian School. He was a powerfully built man with a jolly sense of humor and a tremendous wealth of knowledge. I both loved and respected him, and when he swung down the halls to meetings on his crutches, I always watched him with something akin to awe.

He had been paralyzed in the lower half of his body by an accident as a teenager. But he refused to use a wheelchair. Instead he wore a corset and used crutches in place of his useless lower limbs. His example cemented my determination to live as normally and productively as possible in this formative stage.

These adolescent years brought other changes as well. My family moved to a 120-acre farm in East Rochester near Minerva, Ohio, about 25 miles southeast of Hartville, to join a new church that was being established there. This move, along with my best friend Karen switching schools in eighth grade, caused me to branch out in my friendships. These included my eighth-grade teacher James Lowery. He was a profound thinker and pushed us to understand our world and our God outside of the normal boundaries.

My relationship with God since my public confession had been good, but sometimes I still wondered if I might be missing something more. In the summer between ninth and tenth grade, I was given the devotional book *Streams in the Desert*. With a pen and my Bible, I read and pondered the inspirational excerpts every morning. And slowly something came into focus. I did want something more—more of God's righteousness.

The crisis moment came one afternoon as I stood upstairs at the railing outside my bedroom. With sudden clarity, something clicked inside my heart. I saw the holiness of God for what it was, and I saw my own sinfulness in all its crushing reality. I had never really realized the full scope of surrender. How could I serve such a Holy God without fully surrendering to His Spirit working within me?

The quote from Ignatius that had been a part of my quiet reading time that morning trumpeted through my heart. "God has made me bread for His elect, and if it be needful that the bread must be ground in the teeth of the lion to feed His children, blessed be the name of the Lord."

Tears came fast and hot, and I felt as if I could hardly breathe. The world seemed to reel with the impact of my discovery. Sobbing, I felt as if I were lying in the dust before the throne of mercy. I felt a stirring to cry out to Him as never before. I seemed to be understanding spiritual truths I had never seen before.

In anguish I cried out, "God, you made me bread to feed others. I realize I have tried too long in my own strength. I can't, but you can in me. I have professed you, but I want you to have everything, Lord. I want you to have my life. If this means suffering, God, then blessed be your name. I need you to be my life. Make me like you, Jesus. Clothe me in your righteousness. Lord, I'm hungering and thirsting for you. Please fill me with your presence and your peace."

In that moment something lifted. It was as if my Saviour drew near and breathed new life into me—as if the Shepherd was setting aside His rod and lifting me in His gentle arms of love with a delighted smile. Suddenly I could breathe again. Afternoon sun streamed in the window, and the warm light seemed to echo the glow of glory I felt within.

Below me I heard my siblings' cheerful voices. Six-year-old David called to JoAnn and they laughed together. Baby Dewayne fussed in the kitchen, and I heard nine-year-old Judy's cheery voice cooing to comfort him. Joy bubbled up inside me like never before, and I felt like laughing out loud.

Suddenly a passage from John that I had been reading earlier that week came back to me with startling clarity, almost as if Jesus were speaking it to my heart.

"If ye abide in me, and my words abide in you, ye shall ask what ye will, and it shall be done unto you. Herein is my Father glorified, that ye bear much fruit; so shall ye be my disciples. As the Father hath loved me, so have I loved you: continue ye in my love. If ye keep my commandments, ye shall abide in my love; even as I have kept my Father's commandments, and abide in His love. These things have I spoken unto you, that my joy might remain in you, and that your joy might be full" (John 15:7–11).

My joy was full and overflowing. The following Sunday I told our minister, Leonard Overholt, that I would like to join instruction class in preparation for baptism.

On a cool day in mid-April, I dressed in the traditional black baptismal dress to make a public declaration of my commitment to God and to His body. I knew from our instruction class that baptism was a symbol. But just like wedding vows, it was an important symbol.

I held my white lace handkerchief and a little Bible and solemnly waited for my turn. Two others were in the baptismal class with me.

I had been nervous about the thought of trying to kneel, since that was difficult for me. Bishop Yost Miller had understood, and with his warm smile, he told me to remain seated. With bowed head, I felt the water pour through Bishop Yost's hands onto my head. I thought of the cleansing blood of Calvary, and I felt tears come to my eyes. Jesus had died for me! His blood cleansed me and made me a new creation. It was a sacred, joyful moment.

Later, I wrote a poem on the sacrifice of Christ. I entitled it "Three Crosses."

In the west the sun was setting
In a furious ball of gold.
Red had touched the purple shadow;
Time, it seemed, had no hold.
In the distance towered three gaunt crosses,
Rough in structure, and bold their visage.
Humanity had done its utmost;
Was there a divine plan in this?
Standing 'neath the center cross,
I touched the tree with trembling hands.
It seemed to humbly bend before me;
Oh, the anguish of its stance!
I chanced to see His immortal blood
Drying in a copper hue.
Jesus died upon this cross;
Let us thank Him each day anew.

The final stanza held all the hope I felt when I thought of His resurrection power.

But He arose to live, a glorious Saviour,
In splendor like the crown He wore.
May He rule in your being, this majestic King?
We'll reign with Jesus forevermore.

CHAPTER 10

LEARNING TO LEAN

I felt both nervous and excited as the door opened. My parents and I stepped into the principal's office and were greeted warmly. "Hello, Vera, my name is Mr. Iddings." Reaching out to shake my hand, he suddenly realized I could not lift my arm. Blushing, he gently took my limp hand in his and then turned to shake my parents' hands as well. "We are pleased to have you here today. As you probably already know, I am the principal here at Minerva High School." The slightly built man turned to a taller man standing quietly beside him. "And this is Mr. Cassidy, our fine superintendent." I smiled at Mr. Cassidy, and he shook our hands as well before we sat down and began to discuss the purpose of our visit.

"We would love to help Vera get the best education possible. But we are concerned about her ability to navigate the stairs," Mr. Cassidy pointed out when we had expressed my desire to be enrolled in classes.

"Oh, that won't be a problem," I declared. "I am willing to try almost anything. I manage quite fine in whatever I set my mind to."

"We know at least one student who has offered to help where needed," Dad pointed out. "Vera may find the stairs too taxing, but she would at least like to try to attend classes before we arrange for something else."

"I think we can work with this," Mr. Iddings said, nodding thoughtfully.

"Would you like to be part of the home economics class, Vera?" I could tell he was looking at my covering and plain dress and thinking of my Mennonite background.

I grinned, amused. "Yes, I think I might find that interesting, Mr. Iddings. Thank you so much."

"Of course, Vera. It's been a pleasure to meet you. Your courage and tenacity inspire me."

Before we left the school, I was enrolled for classes that started the next day. That night I could hardly sleep. What would it be like to learn in a public school environment and be surrounded by so many new people? Would I be able to handle the stairs and the physical exertion of full days of classes? Sighing, I prayed and entrusted the matter to God. I was learning that no matter what I faced in life, by far the most important thing I could do, whether I failed or succeeded, was to lean on God.

As I learned to acknowledge Him in *all* my ways and not just part of them, I began to see that He took a vital interest in every detail of my life. He had promised He would direct my path. After planning several details of the day, I handed the situation over to Him and fell asleep.

❧

"Hey, Vera! Good to see you!" Juanita Morrison was a vivacious freshman at Minerva High and a neighbor of ours. She greeted me warmly as we entered the school and offered to help carry my books. I gladly obliged, and when we parted a few moments later, I thanked her for her help.

But I was determined to climb the stairs on my own, a task far more difficult than I had imagined. At home Lena often carried me up and down the stairs to our bedroom. Here, Lena was not with me. As I shuffled up what seemed like an endless mountain of steps, I breathed hard with the effort. Hearing hurried footsteps behind me, I paused, leaning against the railing for support.

"Vera, can I help you?" It was Bernadine Ray, a family friend who attended our church.

"I think I'm okay," I panted.

"Vera, you are exhausted," she reasoned kindly. "I will gladly carry you."

But I was too embarrassed to let her and too determined to conquer the steps above me. "Thanks, Bernadine. I'll be fine." I smiled at her, hoping to convince her.

"Okay." She gave me a worried glance and waited for me as I struggled up the last five steps. When I finally reached the top, I stopped to breathe. I had wondered if I'd be able to make it. My whole body trembled with the exertion.

"I have to run for class, but anytime you need help, let me know and I'll gladly do anything for you," Bernadine offered again.

"Thank you so much, Bernadine. You are a good friend." I smiled at her warmly. Her sincere concern impressed me despite the knowledge that I needed to conquer on my own.

"Oh, no problem," she smiled back. Behind her smile, I saw pain and uncertainty, and I prayed that somehow I could be a friend to her in return for her kindness to me.

Lunch was the highlight of my day. Juanita insisted I sit with her, and she introduced me to all of her friends. They were warm and welcoming, and I thought with pleasure of building relationships with them throughout the coming year.

Home economics class was not nearly so successful. When I saw that the project required adept use of the hands, I sat and watched. *Why am I here?* I wondered in frustration. *I can't even take part. I can't lift my arms, and I look like a fool just sitting here grinning at everyone.* I decided I was not interested in home economics class after all.

Finding my way to the restroom provided another challenge. It was too far away to walk there comfortably, and I felt exhausted when I thought of needing to make the trek every school day.

When I finally arrived home, I had a fierce headache and my whole body hurt with fatigue and stress. "Mom, I can't go back. It's too hard. I almost didn't make it through the day."

Mom looked at me quietly. "It's okay, Vera. We'll arrange for tutors to come here and teach. Just get some rest now. We'll worry about the details later." She hugged me gently and I felt a bit of peace return to my raw nerves. But later in secret I cried. I felt disappointed in myself.

My parents went to see the assistant principal the next day, and the school immediately arranged for me to have teachers in my home. The first tutor arrived the following week, and Mr. Davis and I quickly became friends.

Mr. Davis was tall and personable, with dark eyes and an easy smile. Underneath his easy manner, though, he was perceptive and incredibly intelligent. Within a couple weeks he announced, "Vera, this general high school course is too easy for you. You've already advanced beyond it. What would you think if I asked the principal to advance you to a college preparatory course instead?"

"What would the course involve?" I asked. I was eager to learn, and a challenge was always something I was glad to take on. I sometimes felt that what I accomplished with my brain made up for my physical limitations.

"It would include algebra, English literature, and government, as well as four years of foreign language, preferably Latin and French—although there are several other options as well."

I nodded slowly. "I trust your judgment on that, Mr. Davis. If you think I can handle it, I will do my best."

"I am not concerned about whether you can handle it. I will have to get permission from Mr. Perry, though, before I switch you over."

Within a week we had transferred to the other curriculum. I thrived on the challenge, and as Mr. Davis had recommended, I chose Latin and French as my languages.

One afternoon when we were studying and Mr. Davis needed to look up a word, he inquired where he might find a dictionary. For an instant I was thrown into a conundrum. The dictionary was presently being used as part of the leg to our sofa, since the real leg had broken off sometime before and Dad hadn't had time to repair it yet.

I felt embarrassed to admit where it was, but at the same time I knew it would be a lie if I told him I really didn't know where it was. So, blushing a little, I said, "It's under the sofa there, Mr. Davis."

Without skipping a beat he leaned down and pulled the book out from its book pillar. "Okay, thank you. Now let's see. The word was *transmigration.*" He thumbed through the book quickly as I watched his face with appreciation. He hadn't even acted like anything was out of the ordinary! When he finished defining the word, he returned the book to its place just as casually as he had retrieved it and returned to the lesson without comment. I respected him greatly for his sensitivity and discernment.

Mom always met Mr. Davis at the door with some form of refreshment and an appreciative smile. All my tutors through my high school years would receive the same respectful reception. Most of them became a part of my family in some way. It came to the point where Mrs. Viola Trubee received my sisters' pranks as well as their love.

One day while we were studying a particularly hard geometry problem, a clanging alarm rattled to life at our feet. Mrs. Trubee was so startled she jumped in her chair. "Mercy! What is that?" she exclaimed in fright. I caught sight of Delilah's laughing face pop around the corner of the door just then and glared at her, but only for a moment. The situation was quite funny. When Mrs. Trubee recovered, she chuckled and I giggled with her.

It wasn't just my life that was changing. My siblings' lives were changing as well. Bernadine attended our church consistently now, and I noticed that my quiet, steady brother Fred was taking an interest in this girl. I waited to see how things would unfold.

Fred wasn't the only one interested in romance. Ruth had begun to talk about Johnny Miller. I had first met Johnny at a wedding in Virginia Beach, Virginia. It took a bit for me to become convinced about him.

Whenever I remembered that first meeting with Johnny, I had to laugh. I had been standing a bit apart from the milling crowd of people after the wedding ceremony. One of the things I loved to do most was watch people. Johnny noticed me and came over to talk to me. I pretended not to know that it was because of my neck brace, heavy limp, and small stature that he had picked me out of the crowd. I always did this when I met new people. I acted as normal as possible to prove to them that I was just that—normal.

Johnny's eyes twinkled in a kindly face as he introduced himself. "Hello, I'm Johnny Miller. And you are?"

I smiled up at him graciously. "Vera Overholt," I responded. I felt not the least bashful despite never having seen him before. He was easy and non-threatening.

He grinned. I wasn't sure what all was behind that smile, but I knew there was more than he was saying. "You know," he leaned toward me casually, "that you won't be allowed into the reception area unless you are married, right?"

I was nonplussed by this announcement. "What? Are you sure? But I thought . . . I didn't know that." But as quickly as the words left my mouth, I understood the lurking shadow of mischief behind his smile.

"No, actually not. You're fine." He was laughing and I couldn't help laughing with him. It reminded me of a joke my sisters or I would have pulled on someone else. We chatted for a bit before he drifted away to visit with others, but I didn't quickly forget him. When Ruth met him and they began to talk of a relationship, I held back, thinking no one was good enough for my oldest sister.

Johnny had a way about him, though. He knew how to get into my good graces without my knowing how. When I finally decided that he would be okay, he went the extra mile and bought me a blue parakeet. I fell in love with the parakeet and told Ruth that Johnny would do just fine.

The fall of my senior year of high school, Fred and Bernadine were married. It was a mixture of bittersweet emotions for me. I was blessed that Fred was devoted to God and that Bernadine had joined our family, but in some ways I felt as if I had lost a family member as well when they moved to Three Rivers, Michigan, where Fred would work in 1-W service in a nursing home. Fred had always been quiet, but in ways no other sibling could fill, he had been an anchor to me. Now, more than ever, I was learning to lean quietly on the Lord for strength and purpose.

In the midst of all this change, our love for adventure remained unchanged. After learning to drive in the truck, I decided I would teach my younger sisters how to drive as well. JoAnn was my accomplice that bright spring day when we got into the car. Mom was home working in the kitchen with Lena when they heard the crash. After the car and the picnic table met each other in an unseemly fashion, I decided to leave the driving tutelage to someone else in the family. My parents both condoned this as wisdom, and I gave up driving for good.

One other mishap that would haunt me for years included Michael. We all spent several afternoons a week down at the pond throughout the hot months of summer and fall. One day as we were enjoying lemonade JoAnn had just brought out from the house, we all got caught up in the jollity and excitement of the moment and forgot to keep an eye on little Michael.

He had been happily playing in the sand at the edge of the pond. With no thought or realization of his danger, he crawled out into the water, cooing at its coolness. Unable to swim, he sank under the water only to resurface, choking for air. But no one heard or saw him.

A moment later when I glanced up from my glass of iced lemonade, I took in the empty beach and exclaimed, "Where is Michael?"

Lena threw down her glass, splashing lemonade everywhere. Sprinting as fast as her agile legs would take her, she screamed. In an instant I saw what she had seen: a little body floating face-down, unmoving on the water's surface.

Desperately, I began to pray silently as Lena rushed into the water, grabbed his body and pulled it to shore. JoAnn screamed and turned white, covering her eyes with her hands. Delilah seemed frozen, unmoving, horror written all over her face.

I saw his little face, apparently lifeless with eyes closed. "Lena, pound on his back," I commanded.

Immediately she did what I told her. Still no signs of life. "Turn him upside down and try again," I instructed.

His little body hung heavy against Lena's soaking dress. JoAnn was crying by now and Delilah was helping as best she could. While Lena held Michael up by his feet, Delilah pounded fiercely on his back.

Suddenly he choked and gagged. Water spewed from his mouth, and he threw up again and again. His eyes opened and he looked bleary. When the vomiting subsided, Lena held him close against her shoulder. We all cried a little. "God saved his life," I said quietly.

Somberly, we all headed for the house. We had had enough swimming for the rest of the week. Michael seemed unhurt by the incident, but it would be a long time before I could enjoy the pond without thinking of those dreadful moments of suspense on the water's edge.

CHAPTER 11

WHAT WILL MY FUTURE BE?

Spring sunshine filtered through the cloud of pink cherry blossoms above us. A male house finch, his red head thrown back to the blue sky above him, sat on a branch of the cherry tree singing his heart out in a jumble of short, warbling notes. Mom had just come from the house with iced tea for Miss Hazen and me, so we were taking a break in our Latin lesson.

"He's got a mate somewhere in the bushes near the house," I confided. "I saw them building their nest last month."

Miss Hazen smiled. "Ah, the secrets of spring. But not everyone takes the time to observe them, Vera. The beauty of life often slips by us unnoticed."

I processed this idea thoughtfully as I sipped my tea. Miss Hazen always seemed to have some new wisdom to share. She had taught at Minerva High School for over thirty years and had become almost legendary in the community because of her illustrious teaching career. With a master's degree in Latin from the University of California in Berkeley and a summer of study at Harvard, she was among the elite in our teaching community.

But it was her unassuming, gentle spirit and her tenacity in spite of advancing arthritis that was slowly and painfully crippling her hands and knees that made me admire her the most. Learning Latin in the afternoons with her was always a highlight.

In these last years of high school, I was pondering my future more than I ever had before. Suddenly life was opening up before me, and I wondered what I'd do after school was finished.

It was my English literature teacher, Miss George, who made the biggest impact when it came to encouraging me toward a particular career path. She was young, not much older than me it seemed, and yet her professional precision in teaching gave me a high regard for her. We shared a special bond. Often, when my future came up in that final year of school, she would urge me to consider teaching. "Vera, you are a powerful communicator and you love people. You would make a wonderful educator. I really think you should consider becoming a teacher," she would tell me.

It was a somewhat new idea for me. I listened and thanked her for her confidence in me. But I still wasn't sure what I wanted or what God had planned for my life.

In May of my senior year, Johnny and Ruth were married. Ruth asked me to be her maid of honor, and I readily agreed. It was a beautiful day and I was delighted in my sister's joy. I had never seen Johnny quite so happy, either. But when I hugged Ruth goodbye, my heart ached.

Even though Fred's wedding had felt like an adjustment, I knew I was gaining a sister. Now with Ruth getting married, I felt more like I was losing a sister, even though I liked Johnny and respected him deeply. They would be moving to Zanesville, Ohio, and I knew I'd miss my cheerful, spirited, steady sister dreadfully. In bed that night I confided my feelings of loss to Lena. She listened quietly and agreed, and then she whispered, "But there are more adventures waiting, Vera. Just think of all we want to do with our futures and you won't feel sad for long."

I knew she was right. I pondered my high school years and all the changes they had held. Many changes had happened, not just in my family and in my own heart, but also in the world around me.

I thought back to my many lively discussions with Mrs. Trubee, who had challenged me to think through my value system and yet to accept people for who they were. From her I had learned to think critically about my worldview and the worldview of those around me—to validate truth only after asking difficult questions and mining the answers through research and discussion, instead of accepting everything as it was handed to me.

We had discussed everything from Mennonite heritage to Beatle Mania and the Vietnam War. Mrs. Trubee had also taken me to my honorary dinner and ceremony for the National Honor Society. When I first received the announcement in the mail that I had been chosen to be inducted into the society, I hadn't known what it was.

I called Bernadine and asked her for an explanation. Her response had been sheer excitement. "Oh, Vera, that is one of the highest honors you can receive in high school! You get this honor only if you have at least a 3.5 grade point average. And that's not all—you also have to match criteria based on integrity and ability to lead. I'm proud of you, Vera!"

With my passion for education and learning, I'd been humbled and delighted all at once to receive this unexpected acknowledgment, despite the fact that I studied at home.

The day of my graduation was hot. June 9, 1967, marked my passage from one season to the next. The grand music of "Pomp and Circumstance" was played as all the other students filed in. I and another graduate who had been injured in a football accident had already been brought in before the ceremony began. The superintendent came down off the stage to bring me my diploma and a rose. I held the rose gently between my fingers and whispered my thanks.

At the end of the ceremony, the graduates were all supposed to move their tassels from one side of their caps to the other, signifying their new status. I wondered how I was going to move my tassel, but I wouldn't have needed to worry. Just at the right moment, the girl behind me whispered, "I'll flip your tassel for you." I smiled my gratefulness to her. After the congratulations and thanks to teachers who had given me so much over the last four years, I left with my parents, physically exhausted by the ordeal. I was ready to go home and rest.

But not for long. I was so used to being busy with study and books that I decided to continue as much as possible. I had a giant list of books I wanted to read through, and this kept my mind occupied when it came to continued learning. But despite this effort to reserve a sense of normalcy, I felt a slowly enlarging ache for something bigger. It was time to expand into the larger world, to do something useful by serving others, and to determine just what I was capable of in the real world.

Despite this underlying restlessness, life did hold plenty to keep me busy. Lena and I decided to take a road trip to Michigan that summer to see our first nephew. Fred and Bernadine had named him Freddy after his father, and my heart fell in love with him immediately. His soft, fuzzy head nestled against my cheek, and I rejoiced in his tiny fingers curling around mine.

"Oh, Lena," I exclaimed to my sixteen-year-old sister, "don't you think he's just the cutest baby that was ever born?"

"For sure," Lena agreed staunchly. Then she giggled. "We sound like doting old grandmas, Vera."

"Doting aunts are probably almost the same thing," Bernadine laughed, coming in just then. "I'm so glad you girls could come and visit us. It's been such an encouragement to both Fred and me."

"We are glad we got to come," we responded in one breath. "We wouldn't trade time with our nephew for anything." I was getting my first taste of what it would mean to love my nieces and nephews in years to come, little realizing that the ecstasy I was tasting now would become one of my greatest joys in a very expanded sense.

At home again, we decided to camp on the hill behind the house as we sometimes did together. Lena had finished the sewing for the week, and JoAnn had baked extra pies and cookies. The house shone where Delilah had applied her cleaning expertise and pizzazz on every window, floor, and lamp shade. Judy had finished her work in the barn, and I had done what I could wherever I was needed. Now we needed a party.

"We should invite friends," we decided. That night after dusk, we all bedded down under the stars. Fireflies flitted here and there in the gathering darkness, and in the woods somewhere behind us an owl hooted. We giggled and rustled as we settled into our blanket nest. Dad had extended the cords for my respirator out to where we were staying for the night. He was almost always supportive of whatever ventures we tried, just as he always had been.

"Look, there are the Seven Sisters," Lena pointed out.

"And now *we* have seven sisters," I laughed. "Bernadine brought our number to completion."

The other girls joined in as we continued to identify various constellations.

I had adventures with my brothers as well. Once on a ride to one of our many youth functions, Leon was driving. He was just learning to drive in our old Pontiac, and he took it a bit too fast over one of the Ohio hills. The car actually left the ground, and all of the passengers hit their heads on the car roof. The only person who didn't was Leon. He looked around at us all apologetically when the car wheels were grounded again. Everyone burst out laughing. Then Lena noted that there was a dead fly right above me on the ceiling.

"Oh, look! Vera has killed a fly! What a marksman you are, Vera!"

I looked up in surprise, only to realize she was right. I had been waving the fly away just as Leon had sailed over the hill. It obviously went up with the rest of us. And my sixty-five pounds had gained enough gravity to smash him flat. All of my siblings burst into uproarious laughter. I, however, was not impressed.

"Did it leave a spot on my covering, Lena? Stop laughing at me and help me." I was upset at Leon for his carelessness and a little more than shaken by the wild ride. But good graces were restored within moments, as they usually were in our family. No one ever pouted long. There was too much good fun to be missed.

On a fall day another invitation for fun stirred my blood. "Wanna go squirrel hunting with me?" David's young face was a pleading grin.

"Of course I want to go," I agreed readily.

"You'll have to be really quiet, though." He loved shooting squirrels with his pellet gun, and as was typical of our family members, he was quick to involve me in his world. Ever since we'd moved to the farm in East Rochester, my brothers had enjoyed the hardwoods there. They provided abundant hunting grounds for my eager young brother's nature-loving heart.

The day was pleasantly warm when we set out for the woods. Birds sang in the trees, and the long rays of afternoon sun filtered through the shadows of the long limbs stretching above us. David was strong despite being young, and I was quite light. He carried me to his chosen spot and set me down with my back against a tree trunk.

"We shouldn't talk at all. Hear that chattering?"

I watched the birds flitting from limb to limb above us. I traced the pattern of grass and leaves at my feet. I watched David's intent face as he scanned the trees above us, his body positioned in a ready posture. Every now and then he smiled at me, his eyes warm and shy at the same time. It was one of those bonding moments you don't forget.

He shot two squirrels, and when the shadows started to lengthen and my limbs felt stiff, he decided it was time to return home. As he carried me out of the woods toward the house, I asked him, "Was I quiet enough for you, David?"

"You were great, Vera. I'll take you again sometime if you like."

I grinned. Some of my most memorable and epic moments happened when one of my siblings carried me, like this warm one with David, but more often the hilarious ones with Lena.

One day we were sewing with friends in East Rochester. "Oh, dear, I ran out of blue thread," Lena discovered. "I'll have to run to the store and get some more. I was so hoping to finish this dress this afternoon."

"I'm going too," I added hastily. Lena and I rarely went anywhere without each other.

"Sure." Lena picked up my slight frame in her strong arms and carried me down the front steps. When we reached the road, she looked at me and grinned. "I think I'm going to run. I really am in a hurry to finish that dress." She ran clumsily, cradling me in her clasped hands. She was a sprinter, but

As a child, Vera Overholt spent many days in the Aultman Hospital in Canton, Ohio. Here Nurse Barbara Gaston is holding Vera by the head to support her and keep her from falling. Mrs. Gaston was one of Vera's favorite nurses.

Vera, in third grade, attended Hartville Christian School. She went at noon each day and stayed until the end of the school day.

Vera's father Victor donated the land on which this school was built and helped erect the building with the agreement that his children could then attend there without him needing to pay tuition.

Polio Victim, 5, Marks 489th Day in Aultman

Vera Overholt Uses Her Feet, Toes To Play With Dolls, Toys

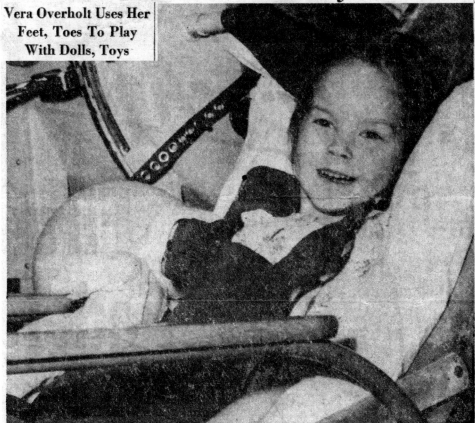

In good spirits in her reclining wheel chair is Vera Overholt, who is today spending her 489th day in Aultman Hospital fighting polio. With her toes and feet, she can play with her dolls, start her phonograph and turn the pages of books. Her arms are paralyzed.

For nearly 500 days, home has been Aultman Hospital to a 5-year-old girl from RD 1, Uniontown.

Today marks the 489th day that polio - stricken Vera Overholt has looked out at the world from the windows of Aultman Hospital.

During that period she has never visited her real home.

-:-

VERA'S PARENTS, Mr. and Mrs. Victor Overholt, visit her each night. Sometimes, according to hospital spokesmen, the parents bring her a little sample of home cooking. That's a little contrary to policy, but if it is something the girl can eat she is allowed to have the food.

On Aug. 5, 1952, Vera entered the hospital. For the last 10 months her home has been room 474 in the McKinley IV wing.

Both of her arms, her back, chest and neck are paralyzed by polio. Her legs aren't affected, but they are not strong enough to support her in walking.

Since her illness, the physician handling the case has said that Vera has become quite proficient in the use of her feet and toes. She uses them to take the place of her hands and fingers, which can't be manipulated easily because of the paralysis of her arms.

-:-

VERA CAN PLAY with dolls, start her little phonograph and turn the pages of books with her toes.

A great pleasure of Vera is the popsicle she receives each afternoon. An ice cream company has arranged to present her with one every day.

afternoon in an iron lung and sleeps in the lung at night.

-:-

ARRANGEMENTS are now being made with the National Foundation for Infantile Paralysis, according to the doctor, for an iron lung to be placed in the child's home. If the lung can be made available, the doctor indicated that Vera may possibly be able to leave the hospital in the near future.

If she can leave, then Vera would be able to see her five brothers and sisters at home. They are Ruth, 7; Fred, 6; Leon, 3; Mary Magdelena, 2, and Joan Patricia, 9 months.

Overholt farms and during the winter months also does masonry work.

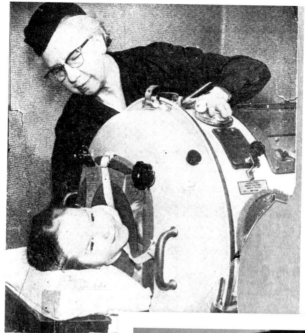

Vera and an official from March of Dimes shown on a March of Dimes poster.

Vera loved holding baby Delilah with her legs. Due to the severity of her paralysis, Vera did not breathe naturally while she was asleep. (She had to consciously think of taking breaths.) The hose she holds is attached to a machine that drew her chest in and out while she slept.

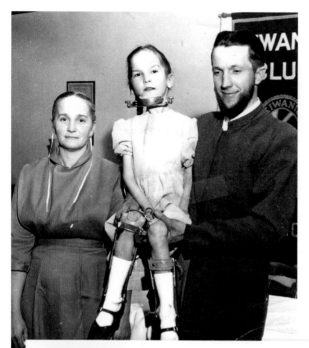

Vera with her parents, Victor and Emma, soon after she came home from the hospital.

The Overholt home in Minerva, Ohio.

Vera's graduation

Vera, age 18.
Her formal
graduation
photo.

Some of the Overholt siblings in 1978:
JoAnn, Vera, David, Lena, and Deliliah.

Vera was 26 years old when she, Lena, and JoAnn visited Switzerland,
Germany, Holland, and England.
   This photo was taken near the stern of the *Queen Elizabeth II.*

Teachers at Minerva Christian School:
Esther Smith, Vera, and Philip Stoltzfus.

Vera loved to plan parties with her students.

Photo taken at the fiftieth wedding anniversary of Vera's parents. Mother Emma Overholt is shown with daughters Delilah, JoAnn, Lena, Vera, Ruth, and Judy.

Vera on "Molly," meeting Joni Eareckson Tada. Molly is the standing wheelchair that Vera's father designed and welded just for her.

Vera

with my added weight she couldn't go nearly as fast. Still, she was making good progress. I laughed into the wind and wondered how it would feel to run alone.

Suddenly I was jolted out of my merriment as I was flung to the hard ground. Dust flew up around me as I landed sitting down with my elbow sprawled out. I coughed and tried to breathe. Lena rolled over and sat up. "Are you okay, Vera?" she asked anxiously.

"I think so," I gasped.

She breathed a sigh of relief and got up, brushing the dirt off her skirt. Picking me up, she shook her head. "I guess I'd better just walk. Haste makes waste sometimes."

I readily agreed, shaken from my tumble, but no worse off than a bruise or two. After a few moments, the humor of the situation surfaced. "At least you don't drop me on the stairs," I laughed.

"Now, Vera!" Lena exclaimed with mock severity. "I never drop you on the stairs even though you almost make me!" She carried me upstairs almost every night to our second-story bedroom. I usually found some dry comment or humorous joke to tell right in the middle of our ascent. By the time we were halfway, Lena would be in stitches and she would have to stop on the stairs to recover before she could finish the climb. "Vera! Stop! You'll make me drop you," she'd gasp between fits of laughter. I would laugh too, and then we'd both laugh some more. She never did drop me on the stairs, though.

CHAPTER 12

UNDAUNTED

"I can't see a thing through this windshield!" Lena declared in frustration. "This snow storm is almost as thick as a blizzard!"

I peered out the windshield from the passenger side of the black Comet as we inched forward on the icy roads. "Just don't miss our turn," I cautioned.

"I think we're already lost," Ruthie declared from the back seat.

"Maybe we should pray about it." Patricia's suggestion was the best one yet. We all paused to ask God to protect us and bring us safely to our destination.

We were on our way to Messiah Bible School in Carbon Hill, Ohio, for a term of study. Ruthie and Patricia Overholt, cousins of ours, had been excitedly planning to go with Lena. As she always did, Lena had insisted that I should seriously consider accompanying them as well. I hadn't given it a second thought. If Lena could go, I was certain I could too. So we'd planned and sewed and anticipated for several months that fall, waiting for the beginning of the term when we would make the four-hour trip south. Most of the ride had been relaxing and enjoyable, as we sang, laughed, and talked together.

But when the storm hit, things got nerve-wracking. Being lost in a snowstorm had not been a part of our plans.

"I think we'd better turn around," Lena said nervously. But the rest of us encouraged her to keep going forward, however slowly.

Finally we became aware that the snow was letting up a bit. "I think I can see the road again," Lena mused, pleasantly surprised.

Eventually we found our way, and with sighs of relief we pulled into the school parking lot and unloaded our luggage. We were glad to settle in.

Our first day of classes was wonderful. I soaked up the outline for Tabernacle Studies by Dan Byler. I loved the thought that Christ was reflected and foreshadowed in the designs and details of the Old Testament place of worship. I pondered long over the truth that Jesus was the High Priest who had entered into the Holy of Holies and made a way to God for us. I reveled in the reality that we can come boldly to the throne to find grace and help in time of need and that we can enjoy intimate fellowship with God through the new covenant. The Ark of the Covenant was fascinating, but the curtain being ripped apart so we could enter in was far more wonderful yet.

By the evening of the second day, however, my physical pain was beginning to outweigh my enjoyment of the rich spiritual food and fellowship. "Lena, the sores on my chin are torturing me! Seriously, I am beginning to wonder if I'll be able to keep going."

"The bandages aren't helping at all?" Lena examined my sores anxiously.

"No, they don't seem to make any difference. This chin brace and corset work for short periods of time, but I don't think it's going to work to sit for hours like this every day."

"Give it another day or two," Lena encouraged solicitously. "Maybe the areas will toughen up and develop calluses."

I felt dubious, but I wasn't a quitter. However, my premonitions proved well-founded when I developed sores on my back from the corset as well. On the fifth morning as Lena was fixing my hair for the day, I looked at her with tears in my eyes. "I'm sorry, Lena. I just can't do this. I have to go home."

Lena paused in pinning on my covering to answer. "You're probably right,

Vera. But why don't you give it just one more day. If you are still sure by to-night, you can call Mom and Dad to come get you this weekend."

"That's a good idea," I agreed, sighing. "I wish I could stay. I just don't think I can. But at least I tried."

"That's right. You are giving it your best and that's what counts." I could tell by Lena's tone that she felt disappointed, both for me and for herself. My leaving so early meant that she would have to finish out the term without my company.

That Sunday my parents picked me up. I said a tearful farewell to Lena and wished her the best. "Take good notes so you can tell me everything when you get home," I said, smiling through my tears.

"Don't worry, Vera. I will!" She gave me one last hug and then stood and waved as we drove out the lane. I sighed deeply and relaxed against the seat. Despite the sadness of leaving, there was also immense relief. I hadn't realized how taxing the pain and exertion had become. But I hadn't been home for long either before I began to brainstorm about my next experiment. Just because Bible school had been such a challenge did not deter my ever-optimistic heart from dreaming of new horizons.

What came to me one morning was an article in the *Reader's Digest*. I had been hearing about comptometers for several years and knew they were very popular. As the forerunner of the office calculator, they were being used widely and almost anyone who had a résumé stating the ability to use one could find a good office job. I read the article voraciously and decided I wanted to learn to use one.

Later that same week I saw an advertisement in the local newspaper offering training classes in the use of comptometers. Looking up at Mom, who had just come into the living room, I announced, "Mom, I want to learn to use a comptometer. There is a training session available this month. Do you think I can?"

"I don't know, Vera. You know I always tell you that where others use their hands, you must use your brain. I'm not sure it would be worth taxing yourself like that. Why do you want to try?"

"It would open up a host of job opportunities for me," I pushed excitedly.

"You can talk to Dad about it." Mom seemed unconvinced.

Dad wasn't any more convinced, and even my siblings were uncertain that I should or could undertake it. But I insisted. I wasn't going to be dissuaded just because someone thought I was incapable of something. Even if I failed, I knew I had to try.

My parents relented and I set up an interview with the instructors in Canton.

"We think we can teach you to become proficient in the use of the comptometer," they encouraged after they had met with us. I was excited. Maybe this was the answer to my years-long quest for my future calling!

Within moments my elation turned to despair. I realized that the sitting position was just too hard for my body. The same issues that had hindered me at Bible school were once again surfacing. *What good am I?* I thought fiercely as we drove home. My parents were quiet, letting me process my grief in privacy.

My thoughts turned to prayer as the miles slipped by. "God, I can't do anything for myself. I can't even wash my own hair or dress myself. What do I think I am doing, trying to pursue a job? But God, I need purpose. You promised to use my life. I want to be useful, but you have to give me something to do that I can accomplish inside the body you've allowed me to have. God, why is this so hard?"

I felt the discouragement lift a little as I poured out my grief and desire to God. It was as if He looked down tenderly and whispered, "I know the plans I have for you, Vera. Trust me. They are good plans to prosper you and not to harm you, to give you a future and a hope. Rest in that. I will make it plain in time. Remember, life is about knowing Me. You can do that even now while you are waiting."

"Okay, Lord, I'll trust you. But please give me hope. I don't want to give up, but I need strength to keep going."

Through these experiences of wrestling with my own weakness, thinking of God's perfect plan, and taking note of examples of people I had read about in numerous biographies, I wrote a short article for our church youth periodical expressing my thoughts. I entitled it, "Is It Impossible?" The subtitle was a verse from 2 Corinthians 12:9: "My grace is sufficient for thee."

> What though the radiance which once was so bright
> Be now forever taken from my sight,
> Though nothing can bring back the hour
> Of splendour in grass, of glory in the flower;
> We will grieve not, rather find
> Strength in what remains behind.

These few lines from Wordsworth describe exactly the character of the English poet John Keats, who we read found beauty in everything: a grain of sand, a drop of water. It is hard for people to find the "silver lining" in a situation, but here we see that Keats had tuberculosis and died an early death with many other tragedies spanning his short life. Historians tell us that all these hurdles in life helped to bring about his career in poetry.

Some of his poems bring tears to our eyes in admiration for the one who could see infinity in a grain of sand and heaven in a rose petal.

Our cheeks blush in shame as we recall how we have denied Christ by grumbling so many times. The Apostle Paul gave us a wonderful example of having an optimistic view of prison. He led his friends in songs of praise to the One who could deliver them if He so willed. Are we doing all we can to receive His blessings? He has them in store for us, if we only ask. Let's ask Him!

And that's exactly what I continued to do. All through those long days of waiting and disappointment, I prayed. God used this season to draw me much deeper into the reality of His Father heart for me and the joy of simply knowing Him. In this season of waiting, I learned that His grace truly was sufficient and His strength was made perfect in weakness. Though I was still quick to admit to myself that I had more things to learn in the area of counting my weaknesses a joy, slowly I was learning to accept who I was and what God had allowed even when I didn't fully understand His plan.

Sometimes my utter helplessness still overwhelmed me. Others often thought I was fearless, but I knew otherwise. On a sunny afternoon out on the lawn, Johnny and Ruth were visiting and our conversation turned to phobias. From where I lay relaxing on the blanket I added my two cents. "I hate the very thought of having something over my face. I just can't stand it."

"Because you feel like you can't breathe," Lena added.

"That's right," I agreed. "Since I can't lift my arms, it terrifies me to have anything on my face."

"I think you could breathe just fine," Johnny remarked casually.

"No, I couldn't," I insisted.

"How do you know? I'll even prove it."

Before I had time to react, Johnny casually flipped the picnic blanket over my head.

With utter panic, I started to cry and kick desperately as darkness engulfed me and I struggled for breath.

Johnny had intended no harm and he quickly pulled it off again, but it was too late.

I went from fear to fury the moment I saw his face. He was half grinning, but he looked bewildered. "Why did you do that to me?" I screamed. "That was mean!"

"I'm so . . . so sorry, Vera. I didn't think you would really . . ." His words trailed off and he looked nervously around at the rest of the family.

"I told you. You didn't listen," I sobbed. Turning my head away from him, I refused to be comforted. Ruth put her arm around me and tried to soothe me. It would take a bit of time before I could bring myself to forgive Johnny for his prank. But he truly did care, and he never tried such a thing again.

Another thing I struggled with was sitting on a chair. Most people would never have guessed that I couldn't sit normally. But I could not fold my body into the usual posture for sitting. Instead, I would support my weight with my hip while leaning against the seat of the chair. With my other leg braced against the floor and my chair turned at just the right angle, I could manage to sit at the table with my family. To turn my chair just right I would often nudge the chair leg over with my foot. One time this ended in a near disaster.

Johnny and Ruth were staying with us while Mom and Dad were away in Delaware for a week. One night we decided to have fondue for supper. All of us were excited as we took our seats around the table. The preparations had taken a lot of time and thought, and we anticipated a delightful evening meal. I nudged my chair leg as usual to position it "just so." As I did, my foot slipped and I fell headlong, twisted, and was instantly knocked out as the back of my head hit the hardwood floor. In that fateful moment the whole fondue supper was forgotten.

My sisters told me the rest of the story later.

Lena jumped from her chair in panic and ran around the table to get to me. When she saw me lying white and breathless on the floor, she screamed and fainted.

Hearing Lena scream and catching a glimpse of me, Judy ran to the corner of the room behind the refrigerator. She fell down on her knees and started praying and crying all at once. "Oh, Lord, not Vera! Oh, Lord, not Vera. Help her, please!"

Meanwhile Delilah had gotten up to help. Seeing both Lena and me lying on the floor, she froze for a second, her eyes large. Then with an, "Oooh, Vera!" she fainted as well.

Johnny remained calm while the rest of my siblings watched in horror. Having been trained in CPR, he felt he could give whatever aid was needed until help could get there. He counted seconds on his watch, waiting for me to breathe. Lifting my head gently, he noticed that my neck muscles had started to twitch. He elevated my jaw to open my airway, and as consciousness returned, I gulped for air.

When I was fully awake, Johnny carried me to the couch and Lena stayed close by to watch over me. My only aftereffects were a mild concussion and a severe headache. The effects on my siblings were perhaps more severe with the trauma of it all, but we soon laughed over this story as much as we did at all our other mishaps. That was how it was at our house.

Lena often encouraged me to tackle college. "You'd make such a good teacher," she'd prompt. "You know you always help us with homework, and you have a teaching mindset. You are always teaching without even trying. And, you have experience with Sunday school and vacation Bible school."

"I've always dreamed of college. But I don't know how it'd work, Lena. Money is a big issue. It costs a lot to go to college."

"You know, recently I was reading somewhere that if you have a physical limitation but are still able to work, the government will help fund your schooling. Let's look into that possibility some more."

While we waited to find out more, I took a writing course from the Institute of Children's Literature. I enjoyed it so much that I wondered if perhaps I should become an author and produce a children's series. But God had other plans.

Through our research on government funding, we came into contact with the Canton Center for Rehabilitation. They sent me to a specialist for evaluation. They wanted to determine whether I was physically able to work and how far my limitations went.

With trepidation I went to my appointment and then prayed for the answer I so longed to hear. Day after day, mail hour came. When the brown envelope finally arrived, I felt jittery and excited and scared all at once. Lena held up the envelope to read to me all the information on the outside before opening it.

"Hurry, Lena. I don't care what it says outside. What does the letter say?" I urged.

She slit the envelope and laid the letter beside me. The words that gripped me were like a knife to my hopes. "Physically unable to work." I burst into tears. I couldn't help it. I'd had such high hopes for this opportunity.

"That's just not right," Lena fumed. She paced the room rapidly. "It's just not right, Vera, because it's not true."

After a moment of sadness, my grief turned to anger. "Lena, you're right. It isn't true. I don't care what that doctor says. I am going to call the center anyway and see if they can still help me."

The receptionist responded that they were still in the process of evaluating my case and would need several more days before they could give me an answer.

For the next three weeks, I called every few days. I had decided I was not going to give up until they gave me a definite answer. Every day I prayed that God would open the doors of His will to me and that a doctor's opinion would not override the truth. Every day I felt fresh courage to keep hoping. Lena encouraged me doggedly and stood staunchly behind my pronouncement that the doctor was mistaken, and I could work if they would only let me try.

On the seventh phone call, the counselor from the center told me, "We just had a meeting about your case, Vera. We decided that if you called again we'd send you to Johnstown for tests. I guess you called, so it's your lucky day. We'll send you as soon as you can make room in your schedule."

"What kind of tests?" I asked. I was suspicious after my last "test" appointment.

"Tests that are designed to show your personal areas of strength. If you do well and pass these exams, we'll pay for your college education."

Stunned, I paused for a long moment as I fought tears of overwhelming gratitude. Then with a catch in my voice, I thanked him and hung up. The next moment I screamed with joy, and Lena rushed in to hear the news. She laughed and hugged me hard.

My trials were not over, however. The month at the center was daunting. I discovered that it was not what I'd expected in that it focused more on specific careers its residents could handle rather than preparing us for regular college. Most of the capacities were hands-on, and I felt out of my comfort level.

By the second week, I'd made few friends and was struggling with discouragement. When I talked to the resident physiologist, I cried openly in frustration. "I think I made a mistake in coming here," I told him. "I don't want to arrange flowers or paint. All I want to do is teach school." The words surprised me. I looked at the man across from me hopefully.

"Vera, you want to teach school. And that's a very noble calling. But . . ." He paused and my heart sank. I knew what he would say next. "I think you realize that each one of us has limitations. Part of what we do here is to diagnose those limitations for our residents. Do you think that if I had epileptic seizures, I could climb telephone poles for a living? Even if I wanted to, I wouldn't be allowed. It's just like that in life sometimes."

"Are you saying I shouldn't teach?" My words were spoken with forced calm.

"Yes, I guess that is what I am saying, Vera. You have skills and have done so well on your tests. I am more than certain that you will find something you want to do."

That night in bed I cried for a long time. The tears soaked my pillow and I wrestled with God. "Give me hope to hang onto, God. I can't keep doing this. Every time I try to find answers, my hopes are crushed. I am so afraid that I'll end up living a useless life. I don't want that to happen. God, where are you?"

"Be strong and of good courage." The words I'd read from Joshua that morning soothed my heart. Suddenly I stopped crying. "I don't care what that man says. I can teach school, Lord. You know me better than anyone. You know how much I want to teach. That man knows hardly anything about me. I'm sorry for letting him discourage me, Lord. Just lead me and I'll follow you." With a peaceful heart I fell asleep.

I continued with the program, determined to give it all I had. Although the tasks they assigned were quite difficult for me, they were not impossible. I graduated successfully from the program and was granted the funds for college. On the drive home from the center, Lena and I chatted and laughed. It was so good to be together again!

Lena looked over at me with a big grin on her face and announced, "Now that you have money for college, I know what you are going to do!"

"What?" I laughed.

"You're going to go home and teach in our school." She sounded convinced.

"I have been thinking about that. I discovered while I was at the center that I really do want to teach, and I think maybe that's what God has planned. But how will it work?"

"Well, after you get your teaching certificate from Kent State Extension in Salem, you shouldn't have any other hindrances to overcome. And when you're in college, one of us will go with you to your class each day, and you can study the rest of your subjects from home."

I looked at her with admiration and delight. "You are right, Lena! I can do this. I will do this through Christ who strengthens me!"

"Whoopee! You are going to be a teacher!" Lena pounded the steering wheel with happiness.

I laughed in sheer relief. At last God's plan was clear! With Lena's confidence, the last barriers had crumbled.

That fall I began to attend college as planned. JoAnn, who was doing high school at home, took me to my classes. Since I took classes only several mornings a week, I was able to tolerate the schedule better than the all-day Bible school schedule. Sometimes challenges arose, but I always went back to that defining moment in the car with Lena and plowed ahead. With God's help I would finish preparing for the future He had planned for me, undaunted by the obstacles. He had promised me a future and a hope, the kind of hope that withheld no good thing from those who loved Him. Through my weakness He was proving Himself strong, and I knew beyond a shadow of a doubt that His purposes would come to pass. He would finish the work He had begun, and I could rest in that.

CHAPTER 13

CHRISTMAS IN BELIZE

As the plane landed and rolled toward the small airport, I felt excitement well up inside me. We were in Belize! I couldn't wait to get out onto the tarmac after the crowded, bumpy flight. But more importantly, I couldn't wait to discover the dripping tropical world beyond the plane window.

Johnny and Ruth had moved to Belize for mission work that summer of 1970. Almost right away I had started planning a trip to see them. When discussing the matter with Mom and Dad, we had all decided it would be special to be with them to celebrate their first Christmas in a foreign country, so they wouldn't feel so alone. Our travel group included Mom, Dad, Lena, and Johnny's brother Jimmy. I looked forward to seeing my sister Ruth again, but I was very excited about seeing my two-year-old niece, Vicky.

"Lena, do you think Vicky will remember us?" I asked worriedly.

"If not, she'll soon be reacquainted with us," Lena reassured. "Oh, there they are, Vera!" I strained to follow her pointing finger through the deplaning passengers and caught a glimpse of them waving at us.

Steam rose from the tarmac as the humid warmth of the tropics swirled around us. I felt as though I had stepped into a sauna. Breathing was hard in the oppressive air. The national airport personnel crowded around me, greatly interested in touching my respirator, which was encased in a brown suitcase of its own. They seemed to be trying to help me and make me comfortable, but I simply felt claustrophobic.

We made our way through the crowd of bodies to Johnny and Ruth. "Welcome to Belize!" Johnny greeted warmly.

"Ruth!"

"Mom! Vera! Lena!"

"Vicky!"

There were hugs all around, and then Johnny showed us to the truck we'd be riding in. A mattress padded the bottom of the truck bed for extra comfort. "The roads are pretty bumpy," Johnny warned apologetically.

As we wove our way through the potholed streets of Belize City, I watched the bustle and chaos with intense interest. Vicky cuddled beside me in her mother's lap, still a bit shy but warming up quickly. "Puppy!" She pointed to a limping black dog in front of a boarded-up shop.

"Do you like puppies, Vicky?" I smiled at her and she grinned back.

Four-by-fours sped through the streets, unmindful of the jolting potholes. Buses belched past. Endless streams of people ambled, rode bikes, stood in shop doors, and bartered at street corners. Loud music thumped from speakers stacked in an open doorway. Horns blared. A baby cried. Brakes squealed. Everything was a chaotic blend of swirling sound and newness.

"This is the Belize City Market," Ruth told us as Johnny parked the truck. "We need to pick up some supplies for the mission."

Piled high under long rows of open stalls, every kind of fruit and vegetable seemed to be available for purchase. There were bright bunches of yellow bananas and piles of green plantains. Mounds of coconuts sat next to blue plastic bags of peanuts and stacks of ripening pineapples and reddish-orange mangoes.

Open tables stacked with fresh, raw fish filled the air with a fishy stench that mingled nauseatingly in the heat with fuel fumes and the smell of rotting trash and overripe fruit. Bright scarves and clothes and jewelry adorned other stalls. Every shopkeeper seemed eager to sell us something. They called out to us in English Creole, cajoling us to stop and look. I loved the thick accent and varied sounds that flowed off the tongues of the national shopkeepers, mixing with their warm, friendly smiles. The riot of colors and the constant ebb and flow of dark faces and bright clothing, smells, sights, and sounds mixed with stifling heat made me dizzy with stimulation.

The ride out to the mission in Cayo was long and painful. Located just east of San Ignacio, it was a seventy-mile drive from Belize City over rough roads. My whole body felt drained and bruised by the time we arrived. When Lena and I were shown to the little thatch-roofed guest house where we would be sleeping, I felt ill and longed to lie down and sleep. After washing our hands and faces in a basin and changing out of our dusty travel clothes, however, I felt a bit better.

Despite the fact that there was no indoor plumbing or temperature moderation in our little house, I felt immediately that it was a friendly place. It was such a relief just to be out of a moving vehicle and on solid ground again.

Our first Latin American supper was tasty, but I was too tired to have much of an appetite. Mom gave me a worried look across the table. "Do you feel okay?"

"I just need sleep," I assured her.

As Lena and I made our way through the falling dusk, I looked up at the overcast sky and wondered if it would rain. "It would cool the air, I think," I mused aloud.

"This heat is hard on you, isn't it?" Lena asked.

"A little bit," I admitted.

That night as we settled into bed to the noise of the diesel generator, I grimaced in the darkness. "Lena, I feel like one giant bruise."

"Did you take your pain medication?" I heard her yawn in the darkness.

"Yes, I hope it works. Otherwise I won't sleep a wink."

"We can talk till you feel better," Lena consoled. An hour later we were both asleep.

Early morning sunlight filtered through the cracks in our door and window. Long shafts of golden light fell on the floor. Lena sat up and yawned. "What woke you up?" she asked, tossing her dark hair out of her eyes.

"They must be using the toaster," I responded wryly. "I could feel the air pressure go out in my respirator."

"One way to wake us up on time." Lena stifled another yawn.

"Did you sleep okay?" I asked.

"Certainly did. Now I'm ready for adventures. How about you?" She opened the window shutter to let in the natural light. Somewhere a rooster crowed. The sound filtered through above the noise of the still-running generator.

"Adventure is always welcome," I grinned. Now that I was over the rude awakening from the toaster, I felt ready to embrace the day. When we'd finished washing and dressing, we went to join the others for the early morning meal.

Over freshly brewed coffee, Johnny told us about the history of the mission and a bit of what life had been like for them here in Belize thus far. If there was one thing my brother-in-law excelled at, it was story-telling.

The fifty-three acres of cleared land that made up the mission compound were lined by a long row of orange trees on the side facing the road. Their dark leaves wore a layer of fine dust from the road just beyond them. Lena and I were eager to drink in our fascinating surroundings. Village life offered much in the way of exotic experience, despite the simplicity of its life rhythm.

Simple houses were scattered along either side of the Western Highway. In many of the dusty yards, an ugly pig or two rooted for mango seeds and discarded avocado pits in the dirt. Scrawny chickens scratched in the dust looking for bits of grain or insects in the hedges along the roadway. Mangy dogs lazed about everywhere, congregating by twos and threes in the shade when the sun grew hottest.

A local woman in bright, simple dress with her black hair tied in a braid was grinding corn with a hand-cranked grinder. Her dark hand went round and round, patiently and methodically. Somewhere a shrill voice was raised in protest, a showdown between a child and parent by the sounds of things.

Farther along the road, a mother hung her freshly washed clothes over the board fence surrounding her home. Her little boy played happily with his homemade "truck" nearby. It was simply a flat board on wheels, with a tin can fastened by a nail for a cab and jar lids for wheels. The children especially seemed friendly and often waved and called out a greeting.

That evening as dusk fell over Belize, Lena and I watched the sun set behind the mango trees. It touched everything with a magic, rosy light, and my heart swelled with the beauty of it all. Birds twittered sleepily in the trees, and frogs began to trill their night song. Somewhere far off, a howler monkey roared. Smoke rose from the houses across the road as each cooking fire was lit. As we walked back to our little house to sleep, fireflies danced across our path. I yawned.

That second night I thought I'd surely sleep better than I had the night before. I was disappointed. "Lena," I moaned. "Lena, I'm sick."

"What's wrong, Vera?"

"It must have been the food. I need to go outside."

The night air whispered warmly against our faces as we stepped quickly out into the night. A few minutes later, I felt a bit better. As we walked back from the latrine, I looked up at the vast blue-black dome above our heads and breathed in wonder. "Lena, the heavens are telling the glory . . ." Stars blazed out brilliant against the soft darkness. No light pollution obliterated the view in the jungle.

"Wow!" Lena exclaimed softly. "It's marvelous, isn't it?"

The next day I took medication, and my condition quickly improved. Though I struggled to find any appetite in the midst of the heat and the unusual food, I still enjoyed trying the various dishes we were served. I especially enjoyed the delectably smooth, light coffee of the region, served steaming hot three times a day.

One day after visiting some Mayan ruins and an ancient Maya temple, Johnny took us to a small restaurant for lunch. "Vera and Lena, you simply must taste the tamales. You know how often I've mentioned them this past week. I just love them; they're the best thing on the menu."

We both decided to try them. Chicken and vegetables cooked in a soft cornmeal shell were then wrapped in a plantain leaf. I was on my second bite of the new food when a large, dusty hen came strolling through the restaurant doorway and started pecking around the tables, clucking loudly. The link between the chicken in my food and the feathered fowl at my feet took away my appetite. It didn't help that I found tiny black bugs in my ice cubes. I contented myself with watching the others eat.

The next day we drove in the truck to Mountain Pine Ridge Forest Reserve. It was the big sight-seeing venture of our two-week stay, and we'd all been talking and dreaming of it for several days.

Set in south central Belize, the native pine forests and rolling hills of the reserve enfolded us in beauty. Dad said he'd carry me when we started the climb to see the Rio Frio Cave. The path wound along the edge of a river. Everyone's feet got wet, except mine and Vicky's. When we came to the massive cavern's mouth, we all stopped to gaze for a few moments. It was at least seventy feet tall and thirty feet wide. Thick tangles of vine trailed down the rock face and scrambled over the top of the opening.

"That is one big cave!" Philip exclaimed in awe. He was a single, missionary school teacher from Minerva, Ohio.

"It certainly is!" Lena agreed heartily.

"This bank is pretty steep," Dad cautioned as we started to climb the loose gravel incline. "Take it easy, everyone."

About halfway up, his feet slipped. Without warning, he and I were falling. My feet flailed wildly in terror. Johnny would recount later that the look on Dad's face was one of fear, not for himself, but for me.

He twisted his body as he fell and blocked my fall. I landed unharmed in his arms. He groaned a little and asked in a strained voice, "Are you okay, Vera?"

"Yes, Dad. I'm fine. Are you?"

Johnny had reached us by now and so had Mom. "Vera's okay," he assured them. The relief in his voice was evident. Johnny lifted me from Dad's arms and set me down beside him.

"Are you okay, Dad?" There was concern in Johnny's voice, and I looked in time to see Dad shifting his leg, which had been unnaturally folded under him when he fell. A pained look crossed his usually stalwart face, but he said nothing. Sitting up, he brushed off his knees and said, "I think I just need a moment to rest, and then I'll be fine."

He was up and carrying me again within ten minutes. But his leg never quite recovered from the injury his knee sustained in that fall. He would limp for the rest of his life. This was the sacrificial protection he displayed for me in so many ways. I trusted him like I trusted no one else.

When we reached the cave, we stepped into the cathedral-like vault, ensconced in another world. "Look at those stalactites!" Johnny breathed.

"They look like impressive chandeliers," Ruth chuckled.

"This place was part of a Maya burying ground at one time," Philip added.

Huge boulders were strewn here and there. Some were as big as a small house. The little river that flowed through the cave formed pools and little splashing falls along the way. Sunlight streamed through from the other end, lighting our quarter-mile trek to the opposite end of the cavern.

"What a lovely place," I sighed as we descended the embankment.

The others finished the day with a bumpy five-mile drive to a thousand-foot drop. Some of us stayed behind to rest. Lena told me all about it later, including her swim in a tropical pool.

Back in the village, the Christmas season had arrived. We went to church on Christmas morning in a cool basement. We had been told we were allowed to attend church barefoot. On our first Sunday there, the preacher had even been barefoot. We sang the familiar Christmas carols with as much joy as we ever had back in snowy Ohio, despite the tropical heat outside. The story of the greatest gift had new meaning in this humble setting.

Several days later as we packed our bags to leave, I looked at Lena and sighed in gratitude. "It's been so lovely."

"The best time of our lives," she agreed.

CHAPTER 14

SHORES OF MAINE

The sun was just peering over the hills as we sped along. Our old black Comet seemed as eager as we were to be on another road trip. I hummed to myself happily, watching the lovely New England countryside pass on either side of us. It was midsummer and we had planned yet another trip. Lena, JoAnn, and I were on our way to Maine.

It had all started with a conversation about the painter Andrew Wyeth. A friend of our family painted in watercolors, and both Lena and I had been taken with the gentle, sober beauty of his work. He told us he styled his work after the painter Andrew Wyeth, which led us to dig for treasure. Lena painted in watercolor too, and whenever we were curious about something, we researched it. It was no different this time. Several books later, we felt we almost knew the author, and his artwork had taken us in.

"We should go tour the museum in Maine where Andrew Wyeth's work is featured," I suggested suddenly one afternoon.

"We need a road trip after college and school are out for the summer, anyway," JoAnn agreed enthusiastically.

"Let's do it!" Lena whooped. We all laughed and the planning began. We found that Maine had many attractions besides Andrew Wyeth, although seeing the Farnsworth Art Museum and the Olson House was one of the greatest draws for us. We also anticipated the rocky shorelines and romantic quaintness of Maine that seemed to stereotype it in our minds.

July of 1971 was upon us, but the heat of the day was still far away as we pulled onto a country road and continued on our route. We'd left our house at 1:00 that morning, long before the stars had left the sky.

Now, the gravel spitting up under our tires seemed to sing a crunchy ditty of its own. Ribbons of dust swirled up behind us. Lena was driving.

Suddenly she pulled to a stop on the side of the road. Peering at the hood, she exclaimed, "What on earth? Look! I think the engine is on fire!"

"No!" JoAnn and I exclaimed together. Steam—or was it smoke?—was rising from under the hood of the black Comet.

"Get out and I'll see," Lena instructed hastily. JoAnn helped me out of the car, and we stood watching as Lena popped the hood.

"Oh, no!" she moaned. "Well, it's not on fire." Steam billowed up around her. "It's a broken water hose. But what a place to have it happen!"

We all looked up and down the empty road. "Let's get the map," JoAnn suggested. "We can at least figure out where we are." She grabbed it from the front seat where she'd been navigating earlier and spread it out in front of her on the trunk. "Where are we now? I think somewhere down here."

"Somewhere in Connecticut," Lena sighed. "Not anywhere near a busy highway where we can get help. Who knows how long we'll wait here."

"Well, at least we can make it evident that we need help," I suggested optimistically. "We should hang something white out the window as a signal of distress."

"I don't know if we have anything," JoAnn mused. "Maybe tissues."

Meanwhile Lena, having recovered from her initial frustration, had passed on to her typical humor. "The old black Comet, she ain't what she used to be," she hummed as she rummaged for tissues under the seat. "Here is a white flag!"

We all laughed as she put several tissues out the window.

"White flags often mean surrender," I mused. "I wonder what God has planned for this morning?"

"That's so true. You never know what His purposes might be," Lena agreed.

"It's certainly all part of an adventure." JoAnn's eyes sparkled with fun. "Hey, we should sing. It's such a glorious morning."

Climbing back into the car, we joined the birds and sang hymns and sat quietly musing by turns. Snatches of conversation flitted in and out, and all in all a profitable hour had passed when an old yellow car rattled toward us.

As soon as we heard it, Lena quipped, "Help is on the way." And she was right. The car pulled to a stop beside us, and a tall young farmer opened his door and got out. He was whistling a snatch of tune, seeming to be in a jolly mood.

Leaning down to the driver's window, he grinned in a friendly way. "Beautiful mornin', ladies. Havin' some trouble here?"

Lena laughed merrily. Our own joy and his were matched despite our predicament. "Yes, we are having a little bit of trouble. But it is a beautiful day to be alive."

"It's a good day to be born too," the farmer chuckled. "My wife just had a baby boy in the wee hours before the sun came up."

"Oh, how wonderful!" Lena enthused. "Congratulations."

"Yep, we're pretty happy. Cute as a button. But what seems to be the trouble?"

"A busted water hose," Lena said. "I'm pretty sure."

A moment later he came back from looking under the hood. "That's certainly right, young lady. You've got yourself a busted water hose. You'll need a new one. I can take you to town to pick one up if you'd like." He paused.

"I have a buddy who owns a mechanic shop. I'll take you there and then I'll help you fix it."

"We would hate to put you out," Lena protested.

"Hey, really, it's not a problem at all. In this neighborhood, we believe in helping people. Come on, it's not far."

An hour later he was back under our hood replacing the water hose. "Let's make him a breakfast fit for a king," I whispered to JoAnn.

"He certainly deserves one," she readily agreed. With Lena's help and consent, we pulled the Coleman stove out of its nest in the trunk and fired it up.

"Is that bacon I smell?" the young man's merry voice came from under the hood, and we laughed back.

"Breakfast is ready when you are."

After he had washed his hands, he came and sat on the grass and ate heartily from the fried eggs, bacon, and toast we'd made. The birds sang around us and the sun shone warm on our shoulders as we enjoyed the food together. "This is the best meal I've had in ages," he grinned gratefully.

"Well, we really appreciate your stopping to help us damsels in distress," I told him. "You probably wouldn't think it, but you are a direct answer to our prayers for help."

He blushed and shifted nervously. "I just do what's right by my neighbor, that's all." He got up and stretched. "I probably best be going to get some sleep now, ladies. I'll be heading back to the hospital soon." He winked and waved. Getting into his old yellow car, he took off and was soon swallowed in a cloud of dust.

We packed up and reloaded the car. As we got in, we all stopped and bowed our heads. "Thank you, God, for sending one of your angels to help us when we needed it. You are good," Lena prayed aloud, and JoAnn and I agreed in our hearts. The Comet's old engine roared to life, and we pulled back onto the road.

"And off we go for Maine!" we all cheered.

We reached Portland that afternoon and asked around for a good place to stay. The "Blue Door," run by two elderly ladies, was our place of choice, and the delightful hostesses there told us of several local sights we just had to see.

After unloading our luggage, we set out on Route 77 for Cape Elizabeth. Here we visited Two Lights State Park. Rocky Atlantic coastline spread out before us, and the ocean seemed to stretch away endlessly. The white of the lighthouse rose against a deep blue sky. A rocky shore tumbled at its base where a thin line of foam whispered with the ebb and flow of the waves.

"Isn't it just lovely?" Lena exulted.

"It's wonderful!" JoAnn agreed.

"Makes me think I'm dreaming." I breathed the salt air and shut my eyes in rapture.

∽

The next morning we were up early to hunt out our next adventure. "I'd say let's go clam digging on Chebeague Island," I suggested. "The little lady we talked to last night made it sound delightfully romantic."

So we went. Catching a ride on a little boat to the island, we then hailed a small yellow taxi driven by a very small lady with silver hair and a lovely smile. In a deserted cove she dropped us off to try our hand at clam hunting. "I'll be back to pick you up this afternoon." She waved cheerfully and was gone.

"Now to find those clams," JoAnn declared. We headed for the edge of the beach with a soft salt breeze in our faces.

"Look for holes in the mud about as big around as your index finger," Lena said, recounting our hostess's instructions from the day before. "Then dig about a foot down till you find the clam."

"Be careful because the shells are sharp," I added.

"And do it before the tide comes in so you get enough for supper before the evidence of their hiding places is washed away," JoAnn finished.

We set to work, I using my toes and Lena and JoAnn using their fingers. We got fairly quick at it and laughed uproariously over everything and nothing. Finally we decided we had found enough. We sat back to rest and eat our picnic lunch until our taxi ride returned.

Back in our room in Portland that night, we cooked those clams on our Coleman stove. They were splendidly tasty and every bit worth the work we'd put out for them.

We set out early the next morning, heading north. It was time to find Andrew Wyeth's famed paintings. Eighty miles later we stopped at the Farnsworth Art Museum. We knew that the artist made his summer home in the Portland area, and we had also discovered that his most well-known painting was based on a local woman and her farmhouse, called the Olson House.

"There it is!" I pointed out. We stood studying that famed original artwork. The painting was called *Christina's World*. Muted browns and greens of prairie grass formed the background for the girl with her useless legs crawling across the field. She was traveling painfully, slowly, from the family cemetery to the distant farmhouse. A solemn, almost mournful air hung about the picture, yet it also held a note of triumph. The painting held something special for me. I liked it the best of all the paintings I saw.

After several hours at the museum, I turned to Lena. "Let's go see the Olson House," I suggested.

"Certainly," Lena agreed. "We can look for Andrew Wyeth's place of residence while we are at it."

After several wrong turns and asking directions at a gas station, we found the Olson House.

"It's just like *Christina's World,* except alive," I breathed in wonder.

"But not so bare with the trees and other buildings around it." JoAnn seemed to find comfort in this fact.

Inside we gazed at still more of Andrew's gentle paintings. *"Weatherside."* I read a painting title.

"See, there's the Olson House in the painting again," Lena pointed out.

Suddenly JoAnn gasped and whispered, "Lena! Vera! Look outside—there's Betsy Wyeth herself!"

Through the window we watched as a tall, dignified woman came quickly up the walk. Her step was brisk and businesslike despite her informal manner of dress. Upon entering, she immediately straightened a painting that hung slightly crooked on its peg. We knew then for sure that she was Betsy, Andrew's wife. Only the owners would dare to touch the artwork. We pretended to go back to the paintings. But I couldn't help stealing a glance at her every so often. I was sure others in the museum would recognize her and try to speak with her. I was tempted to do the same myself.

"Excuse me, ladies." A congenial, cultured voice behind us halted our discussion over the painting *Groundhog Day.*

Turning, I saw Betsy Wyeth standing there with a warm smile on her face. "Are you girls from Pennsylvania?" she inquired.

"No, we're from Ohio," Lena answered. She and I exchanged a quick glance that said, "Why us?"

"You're Betsy Wyeth, right?" I asked.

"That's right, I am." She smiled again. "I'm sorry if I startled you. But I wanted to ask because we live near Brandywine in Pennsylvania every winter, and we've come to know quite a bit about the Amish people there. My husband Andy is fascinated with your simple ways of life and your lovely dress. He says it fits with his painting style. Simple contrast."

We blushed a little at this comment and glanced at our solid-colored cape dresses. It wasn't often that people made statements about the way we dressed. But Betsy was so sincere and warm that we couldn't help liking her.

"You know . . ." Her eyes suddenly lit up as if a brilliant idea had occurred to her. "Do you want to meet my husband? I think he'd like to see you."

"Of course!" Before we even thought about it, we all agreed eagerly.

"Great!" Betsy seemed to be in her element. "When I leave in a bit here, just follow me. The blue Jeep is my vehicle."

As Betsy turned away, I grinned at Lena and her eyes laughed back. "Wow!" Her lips formed the words without speaking them. Our friends back home wouldn't believe it! We were going to meet the famous painter himself.

Andrew and Betsy's home was down a long lane paved, interestingly, with crushed seashells instead of gravel. The house had gray wood siding, weathered by the wind and the sea that licked at the rocky shore nearby.

We got out of the Comet and waited uncertainly while Betsy disappeared into the house. A moment later she returned with a big smile on her face. She was followed by a lanky man with close-cropped silver hair and a buoyant, long-legged gait.

"Andrew, these are the three Overholt sisters from Ohio: Vera, Lena, and JoAnn. They're fans of your artwork."

"Well, welcome to Bradford Point." His startling blue eyes twinkled in a boyish grin as he surveyed us. "What brings you to Maine?"

"Well, the main reason we wanted to come was to see the Olson House, but we also wanted an adventure, I guess," Lena said honestly.

Andrew laughed. Then looking us over, he changed the subject abruptly. "I love your dresses. Simply elegant. So well made and yet without any extra frills. They are marvelous. Do you make them yourselves?"

I realized that it was his artistic side that made him so fascinated with how we dressed. Lena smiled. "Yes, we make them ourselves."

"You know, I have a Mennonite suit coat that a bishop down in Pennsylvania gave me a few years ago. Let me go put it on for you."

He was gone for only a few moments before he returned, sporting a dark gray suit coat and pants. "I wear it only for special occasions, like visiting the President and visiting with you." He winked at us teasingly. "Do you want to see my studio?"

"Oh, yes!" Eager to see his place of inspiration, we discerned that the artist was easy and personal despite a slight bit of eccentricity.

His studio was a simple building with multiple windows facing the ocean. A large skylight window let in a stream of natural light. "I paint only by natural light," he explained as we stood looking around. On an easel stood a half-finished painting, and on his workbench a mass of paint tubes in buckets held his colors ready for use.

They showed us the house as well. It was simple and spare, but beautifully furnished. As I gazed through the eastern windows at the ocean waves, I felt a new understanding. No wonder he found such inspiration for his art here! He seemed to paint contrast and struggle, yet the conflict of elements was eased by simplicity. His eyes were distant and yet friendly, mischievous and thoughtful by turns. They made me think of the ocean waves, constantly reflecting the moods of the sky.

"Would you like something cold to drink?" Betsy was asking. We all welcomed her offer. It had been a long time since breakfast. When we had visited and enjoyed our cool drinks for some time, we knew we'd have to be getting back to Portland soon. Lena asked them, "Can we sing something for you?"

"We'd love that!" Andrew and Betsy said heartily.

So our trio sang the words of the old hymn, "How Great Thou Art." Sitting there in the quaint living room with the faint sound of ocean waves drifting through an open window, it felt like a fitting close to our visit.

After giving us a signed reproduction of a painting, Andrew and his wife saw us to our car. As we drove away, we all sighed in contentment. "Who would have ever thought?" Lena said aloud.

"Dreams do come true," I said happily. "Now we can say we've met the famous painter and even been in his home."

JoAnn looked at the painting she held in her lap. "We have a signed painting for proof."

We spent a week exploring the coves, shores, and tastes of Maine. We ate at signature local restaurants such as the Lobster Shack, where we exclaimed about the taste of lobster while sitting at a table that overlooked the rocky shore just below us. After each day's adventures, we called home to talk with our family. All highlights of the week were eclipsed by our visit to the painter's house, but we had another uniquely memorable adventure as well.

That evening found us down on the docks watching the lobster boats when a gruff voice from behind us asked, "Would you like to go out lobsterin'?"

We turned to see a weathered, middle-aged fisherman.

"Uh . . . sure," Lena agreed hesitantly.

"Six o'clock sharp be here at the dock," he said brusquely. "See ya then." He tipped his hat and strode away before we could say anything more.

"Do you think we really should?" JoAnn asked worriedly.

"Of course we should. We won't get another chance like it," I spoke up hastily. "There are three of us. We'll be safe." So it was agreed.

We set sail on a tranquil gray sea as dawn stole over the horizon. Gentle waves lapped against the little fishing boat, and the tang of salt air tickled our senses. When we reached the first buoy, the fisherman pulled up the wooden cage and took out lobsters and crabs before dropping it back into the water with a splash. All morning he went from trap to trap, till the boat floor was piled high and the smell of fish permeated everything.

At 11:00 he opened a lunch pail and took out a thermos of coffee and a sandwich. He ate placidly, gulping a swig of black coffee every few bites. He didn't offer to share. And we, having had no idea how long our fishing adventure would be, had not brought a lunch.

By the time we returned to the docks it was early afternoon, and the romance of a fishing trip on the ocean had long begun to fade. We hurriedly thanked our host for the experience and prepared to leave.

He shrugged. "Sure," he grunted. "Didn't mind."

Sore, tired, and famished, we found the nearest restaurant. That night we slept hard. It had been an adventurous day and one we wouldn't soon forget.

CHAPTER 15

TEACHER'S PLEDGE

The fan blew loud in the afternoon stillness, and the air around me felt suffocating. I always found it harder to breathe in the heat of summer. August's hazy blue sky stared through the living room window, and I stared pensively back. *Well, God, what do you want me to do?*

My black and brown Chihuahua, Herky, lay stretched out by the fan, his tiny ribs rising and falling in sleep as he napped at my feet. I'd been dreaming of finding a teaching job ever since my graduation that spring. Reading the monthly copy of the Amish teaching periodical *Blackboard Bulletin* and a magazine for elementary teachers called *The Instructor* only whetted my appetite more. But how would the fulfillment of my dream come? Not everyone would be willing to overlook my limitations and give me a chance.

Lena stepped in from outside where she'd been hanging up wash, and one glance at my face seemed to tell her my thoughts. "You need to call John Sommers, Vera. You know our church school is the place for you."

"Lena, that's not the way it works." I took a sip of my iced tea and looked at her dejectedly. "They are supposed to ask people to teach, not the other way around."

Lena poured herself a glass of tea and came to sit down across from me. "How are they ever going to know you want to teach if you don't tell them? You can't just wait for them to read your mind. It'll never happen if you don't take initiative. You're the one who taught me that, you know." She grinned at me persuasively.

"But it will look like I am pushing myself on them instead of offering. How do I even know they would consider me? If I'm going to teach school, I want to teach for someone I know wants me."

"Fine, Vera, I'll call him. Then it won't look like you are pushing yourself on them." Lena stood up and set her iced tea on the table. "I'm going to call right now."

"Don't you dare!" I exclaimed to her retreating back.

Turning back with an impatient gesture she put her hands on her hips. "Vera, you know what you are supposed to do, and there is no way they will know unless you tell them. You have two options. You can call them or I will call them. But it's one or the other. I am not going to stand by and let this go down the drain. It's what you are called to do."

"I'll call John," I relented, sighing. "You're right. It is what I feel led to do. Give me a few minutes to pray and get up my courage and then I'll call."

She sat down and sipped her iced tea nonchalantly. "You'll do just fine." For once she was much more confident than I.

My heart pounded as I walked my fingers up to the receiver and bumped the cradle off the hook. Laboriously I dialed the number and then waited for the call to go through. *Lord, Lena's right. This is what I feel called to, but I'm so afraid and there are so many "what ifs." Give me the courage and the words to say what I need to say. And please lead me through John's decision.*

"Hello," John's quiet voice answered on the fifth ring.

"Hi, John." I gulped in air. "This is Vera calling."

"Hi, Vera. How are you?"

I didn't waste time on preliminaries very long before I blurted the question.

"I know you are looking for a teacher for the upper grades at the school. Do you think there would be a possibility that I could teach?"

I had said it. Those fateful words could never be recalled. I could almost hear John thinking on the other end of the line, and I waited with bated breath for his reply.

"Well, Vera, it's a possibility. Why don't I talk it over with the board and get back with you?" he asked.

"Thank you. Thank you so much." I hung up the phone and sighed. "Well, at least it's not a 'no.' "

Lena grinned at me in triumph. "What did I tell you, Vera? Of course they'll want you to teach!"

Over the next few days, I waited anxiously. Finally, nearly a week later, John called back. "We're interested in letting you teach, Vera. We can give it a try and see if it works out for you."

After the short phone call, I let out a big sigh of relief and turned to my sisters, who were smiling with me. "Well, I guess it was what God wanted after all. I've dreamed of this for so long. I can't tell whether I'm more excited or just relieved!" I laughed happily. "I'll do my best. I can't wait to start."

I spent the next several weeks feverishly planning and preparing. Lena and JoAnn were my right-hand helpers in all the things I couldn't do myself. I wanted my room to be beautiful as well as educational. Remembering my own years in high school, I chose a piece of poetry by John Greenleaf Whittier as the theme for my bulletin board.

"Still sits the schoolhouse by the road . . ." I quoted from memory. Lena carefully inscribed the first three verses of "In School Days" next to the colorful cutouts of two school children with lunch pails in hand that she'd pinned in the exact places I'd dictated.

"There, Vera. It looks beautiful."

"I love it," I agreed enthusiastically. "The poetry is the best part of all. I can't wait to teach my children the words by heart."

"What if they don't like poetry?" JoAnn asked from where she was putting books in place.

"Oh, poetry is like music. Of course they'll love it once they understand how beautiful and enriching it is," I said confidently. "Say it with me, Lena." Grinning as she wiped a wisp of dark hair out of her face, Lena read off the words in a recitative tone. I joined her.

> "Still sits the schoolhouse by the road,
> A ragged beggar sleeping;
> Around it still the sumacs grow,
> And blackberry-vines are creeping.
> Within, the master's desk is seen,
> Deep-scarred by raps official;
> The warping floor, the battered seats,
> The jackknife's carved initial;
> The charcoal frescoes on its wall;
> Its door's worn sill, betraying
> The feet that, creeping slow to school,
> Went storming out to playing!"

I lost count of how many times I maneuvered down the church basement steps to my classroom in those weeks of getting ready. By the opening week of school, I had begun to feel at home in my classroom.

The school was a neat red brick and white-sided building with a wooded hill rising up behind it. Across from its homey structure, Rochester and Knox School Roads met at a corner. The ground floor formed the sanctuary for our church, Christian Fellowship Church. The basement was where the classrooms of Minerva Christian School sat waiting for students.

The school had been in operation for only six years. Started by Lester and Jean Herschberger with a vision for a godly education for their children, they had stepped into the role of first teachers for the school. I felt a weight of responsibility for the spiritual wellbeing of my students when I considered this heritage. It would require more than just teaching Bible basics and leading devotions every morning. I wanted my students to know and love the Lord for themselves and to see His love in me through my interactions with them. With this in mind, I set out to write a teacher's pledge that would put my longings into formal words. When it was finished, I read and reread it before tucking it away to be read to my students on the first morning of class.

My two sisters, Delilah and Judy, and my brother David would all be students of mine that year. Delilah, who was in tenth grade, also became my teacher's assistant. She would do many helpful things for me such as decorating the bulletin board and writing daily lessons on the blackboard.

In the weeks before school started, they had things to prepare as well. One of these projects was matching blue dresses for Judy and Delilah. "You know I don't know how to sew," Delilah had told me. "But if you tell me how, I know I could do it. I have both dresses all cut out." This was often the way I taught my younger siblings to do things. I learned by observing others, and then I could tell them step by step exactly how something was done, whether it was frosting a cake, baking a turkey, or sewing a dress.

"Okay, thread the sewing machine," I agreed. "I am still working on my schedule for school, but I can do that while you work on each step in between instructions." I watched her slender figure dart through the door and away to fetch what was needed for her project. She was always so lively and full of fun. I looked forward to having my siblings as part of my classroom, but I also felt nervous about it. I hoped that I'd be able to keep from showing partiality in any way.

Looking over my weekly schedule, I changed a detail on Wednesday afternoon's plans and moved math class from one hour of the morning to another. It was nearly completed, but I wasn't quite satisfied with it yet. Something seemed to be missing. Was it too academically streamlined? Maybe I needed to add a bit more creative time in somewhere. As I mused over this problem, Delilah declared that she was ready to start.

"Okay, you are going to take these two pieces and turn them over like this. Then you want to sew them together right along this edge."

"Okay." She began eagerly and was soon well into her project. I finished my schedule and Mom brought in iced tea for us to sip while we worked.

"Are you excited about teaching?" Delilah asked conversationally as she guided the lightweight fabric under the humming needle.

"Yes, I think so," I responded thoughtfully. "It's more hard work to get ready than I expected. But with all the help I've had, I think I am almost prepared."

"You'll do well, I'm sure. Now how did you say to put this skirt on?" By the first day of school, Delilah had sewn two dresses and knew how to sew by herself without my help.

"It looks lovely on you," I affirmed as she and Judy tried on their finished attire. "Perfect for a first day of school."

The morning dawned clear and bright, and I spent extra time getting ready for the day. Everything had to be just right. I felt a mingling of excitement, trepidation, and determination swelling inside me as the moment to leave for school drew near. "I hope your day goes well. Don't tire yourself out," Mom cautioned me at the door.

"Don't worry. I'll be fine," I promised. But inwardly I worried. Would I tire too much to finish the day? There was no going back now; I was committed. I breathed a silent prayer. *God, you called me to this, and I know you are going to help me. Help me in this moment not to fear but to step forward with courage and do what you're asking of me. Help my students to be prepared to receive me as their teacher. And Lord, help me to teach well and to teach my students the meaning of life.*

As each student filed into my classroom, most of them towered above me. At only 4 feet 2 inches and 65 pounds, I knew I was not going to handle them by force. I would have to win their hearts. And that was my goal in teaching even if I had been twice my size.

"Good morning, Ruth Ann. Good morning, Willis."

"Good morning, Sister Vera."

"Willis, this is your desk. Ruth Ann, you'll be sitting here next to Rachel Stoltzfus."

When all twelve of my sixth through tenth grade students had found their seats, I opened the day with prayer. Afterward I took a deep breath and smiled at the expectant faces in front of me.

"I am honored to be your teacher this year," I began. "It is my goal to give you the best education I can as well as to share the joy of learning with you. But before we start into studies, I'd like to discuss a few things."

They listened intently as I practically and briefly explained my limitations and handicap and how I would need their help and cooperation to make things flow smoothly. "And now, I want to share with you a teacher's pledge I wrote for this occasion. I want you to know what you can expect from me as well." I looked down at the crisp white paper on my desk and cleared my throat.

"I solemnly pledge myself before God and in the presence of my students to pass my life in purity and to practice my profession faithfully. I will abstain from whatever is mischievous and will not knowingly administer any harmful doctrine. I will do all in my power to maintain and elevate the standing of my profession and will hold in confidence all personal matters committed to my keeping and all family affairs coming to my knowledge in the practice of my calling. With loyalty will I endeavor to aid the student in his work and devote myself to the welfare of those committed to my care."

I paused for effect. Every eye was fastened on my face. They were listening well. I hoped I was communicating my deep longing to care for their souls and be their friend. After I had read the rest of the pledge, I picked up a pen and signed my name to the document.

After devotions, I spent the rest of the day assigning texts to the various grades, reminding students of school protocol and reviewing classroom procedures. They would be helping me with numerous activities that I could not do myself, such as setting out my textbooks in the proper order for the next class and opening the books to the right pages. I felt that the first day was full of business and structure, yet I felt that my heart was already bonding with my students. They seemed eager to help; it made them feel good to be able to do things for me. I couldn't wait to dive into learning with them!

The highlight of my day was before the final bell when I asked the students to read aloud with me the poem "In School Days." As the story unfolded through verse, I encouraged them to put expression and emotion into the words. "Imagine you were there. What do you see through these words?" I coached.

When I walked into the house that afternoon, exhausted but happy, Mom met me at the door with a worried smile. Two glasses of iced tea welcomed me to the kitchen table. I sat down and squirmed into position. With a sigh, I pulled the frosty glass toward me.

"Well, how was your first day?" Mom asked cautiously.

I took a sip of the sweet mellow tea and grinned. "Just as I planned it would." I took another sip thoughtfully. "I guess I've found what I was meant to do."

Just then JoAnn came in from the living room. She smiled teasingly. "Did your students like the poetry?"

"Ask them," I shot back.

"I'll take some tea," Delilah declared as she came into the kitchen. "And that's the first and last time we'll be wearing those dresses I slaved so hard to make." I saw immediately that she'd changed from her blue dress into an everyday dress.

"What happened?" JoAnn wondered.

"The teacher from the lower grades thought the fabric was too thin. She asked us not to wear them again and sent a note home for our parents." Judy filled in the story as she sauntered in to join the conversation. "I don't know why she felt that way, but like Lilah says, this'll be the last time we wear them to school."

"That's good, girls. I'm glad you respect authority," Mom approved.

"But back to the poetry. Did you girls like it?" JoAnn winked at me and I glared at her.

"Sure." Delilah popped a piece of chocolate chip cookie in her mouth. "She's harder on her siblings than the other students, but her poetry is lovely."

I thought about protesting but I knew I wouldn't win the argument. Judy came to my rescue. "I loved the poetry, Vera."

"Everyone should learn to enjoy its beauty," I agreed.

The three of them drifted out of the kitchen one by one, and Mom smiled at me tenderly. "You should rest now, Vera. Tomorrow will be another big day."

As I lay on the sofa, I pondered the day and prayed for each of my students. I prayed for myself as well, that I would be able with God's help to keep my teacher's pledge.

CHAPTER 16

LEARNING CURVES

Large, fluffy flakes of snow drifted lightly through the February atmosphere. I shivered a little as I entered the schoolhouse with Delilah and Judy close behind me. "Be careful of those cupcakes," I reminded Judy over my shoulder.

"I am," she responded readily. "Don't worry."

"So we are going to celebrate Valentine's Day today." Delilah winked at me and her teasing laugh rang out in the empty school room as we entered.

"I think it will give everyone something good to think about. And it will be a perfect platform to talk about the note-passing issue I've been wanting to address since that incident last week," I responded cheerfully. "And, you know, any excuse to have a party makes me want one."

"Well, these chocolate cupcakes look mighty good," Judy affirmed.

"And every young person needs some romance control," Delilah drawled. She and Judy laughed, and I laughed with them.

"Of course. Who of us didn't have crushes in school?" I agreed. Then, sobering, I added, "But it's not something I want to encourage. Young people should be able to relate in a healthy manner without getting romantically involved while they are still so young. And, it creates problems among the girls when someone is always being teased that 'so and so likes you.' "

"You're probably right." Delilah finished tacking my yellow rose cutouts on the bulletin board, under it the words "True Friendships" drawn in bold, black calligraphy.

Soon other students were arriving. When all twelve of my charges were in their desks, I opened the day with prayer.

"Johnny, will you lead us in the opening song this morning, please?"

Johnny squared his broad shoulders and strode to the front of the room. His strong bass voice led out, "I owe the Lord a morning song of gratitude and praise . . ." Sweet four-part harmony filled the room as each student sang a part. I savored this moment of watching their faces. I had made it a habit to study each of my students as much as possible. It was easier for me to understand and relate to them when I felt I knew what their expressions and body language meant and how their personality related to mine and those of the other students.

After a talk on 1 Corinthians 13 and what the agape love of God means in our everyday lives, I moved on to the morning math lesson. Math and English were my favorite subjects to teach. In math I liked that there was always one right answer. It felt safe and concrete to me. In English, I enjoyed the beauty and orderliness of words that fit together well. I struggled more when it came to teaching science, although I loved medical science and the beauty of the natural world. A history test and a literature lesson from Shakespeare's famous *Merchant of Venice* passed the rest of the morning.

That afternoon I informed my students that because it was a national holiday, I had chosen to plan a special afternoon instead of our normal school. My seventh grade students, Martha and Ruth Ann, broke into happy smiles. Joseph and Mark looked reluctant. My older students grinned and waited.

"Actually, I have something different from the usual in mind. Instead of calling today Valentine's Day, I'd like to call it Appreciation Day. It's easy when you are together all the time to become less cautious and tease and flirt and pass notes, but I'd really like to encourage you to think about things from a different perspective.

"All of you are young, right?"

There was a collective nod. Every face was sober, and several were blushing.

"Recently one of your parents contacted me about a problem they felt was being faced here at school. They shared that they were concerned because of the teasing their child reported that was going on, especially among the girls. I want you to know that from now on I don't want that happening here in our classroom. We can honor and enjoy each other's company without accentuating the subject of romance or teasing about one person liking another. Don't you think?"

Everyone nodded in agreement. "Thank you. I'm glad. I want our classroom to be a safe place where wholesome friendship and fellowship is enjoyed, and it is really up to each one of you to make it happen. Now, how many of you want to have a party this afternoon?"

Sober faces broke into broad grins. "A party? Sure!" The general sentiment was shared by everyone.

"Wonderful." I smiled. "Let's start our party with a formal exercise in appreciation. Each of you choose a partner of the same gender and write a note to that person about how and why you appreciate him or her. Martha, will you help me pass out paper?"

For half an hour, pens scraped busily across paper, often pausing while furrowed brows spoke of concentrated thought. I smiled as I watched the students investing their best in my assignment. I felt a warmth for each of them as I thought of their various strengths and weaknesses. The evening before, I had spent time writing a short note of appreciation to each of them. They had taught me so much! Already my original confidence had been tested. They were cooperative but challenged me daily as I strove to be an example and fill their minds and hearts with not just book knowledge, but also truth.

When everyone had finished writing, the students took turns reading their notes aloud. Despite an occasional blush or uncomfortable shuffling of feet,

I could tell by the happiness in their eyes and smiles that the students were blessed both in having an opportunity to bless someone else and to be affirmed themselves.

"And now for the cupcakes and a talk on what true friendship means," I announced. A collective cheer went up over the cupcakes. They were quickly devoured, but not without manners. That was another thing I insisted on in my classroom. We had a lively discussion on friendship, and we finished out the day with a new camaraderie and unity among us.

On the way home that afternoon, Delilah seemed in a more introspective mood than usual. "Vera, do you think you'll get married someday? I mean, Fred and Ruth are married now. Do you like being single or do you want to find someone and have your own home and family?"

"I guess I don't know, Delilah. Sometimes I think I'd like that. But I'm not sure I ever could." Her question brought longings to the surface that I had ignored for a long time. Would I ever get married? I knew my limitations would be a huge hurdle. It wasn't completely out of the question, but I didn't count on it happening either. Early in my teen years I had learned to be practical about reality, despite my consistent optimism that I could try almost anything I desired to.

As I pondered this, I realized that I really was content where I was. I loved teaching. I loved investing in the lives of my students and siblings. I loved learning and traveling. My life held many wonderful elements. I was truly blessed, and I knew that despite occasional longings, I would continue to be content. I had chosen this path, and this was where God had called me.

⌒

"Sister Vera, it's not fair. I've had to stay in for two recesses in a row now just because the other two students in my grade didn't get 100% on their math quiz. I got 100% both times."

"Stay in this time. I'll think this over," I responded thoughtfully. My grading system seemed to be causing some complications. I had set up a reward system based on an entire grade's scores. If an entire grade got 100% on that week's chosen subject, they got to go out for recess. If not, they were kept in and given extra problems to work on. Now it had come to my attention that it was causing frustration on the part of my students who excelled. When those who were naturally less inclined toward a particular subject didn't score as high as they did, everyone suffered. I hadn't foreseen that this would be an issue.

My original purpose had been to encourage healthy competition and group accomplishment. I was quickly learning that I would have to find another way. My motivation to make a complete switch in my system came when I discovered that one of my less academic students was being taunted by those who had to stay in because of his failure to perform. From that week on, I graded students on individual performance and rewarded them accordingly. Occasionally I had the class work together on a project to earn rewards, but I never had it as my main system again.

Despite this switch, I required much from my students. They rose to meet the challenge, and I was rarely disappointed in them. Discipline issues were rare that first year. I would face much more in the years to come, especially after I switched to the younger grades, but that first year marched by like an orderly row of soldiers with little variation in plan and minimal struggle.

Unified relationships, not just among my students but among my community and family as well, seemed to be a growing theme in my reflections. Friendships were of utmost importance to me. I couldn't understand why people separated over trivial issues and squabbles.

Over Christmas that year, there was some tension in the church membership. As I often did, I responded to the conflict and tension with poetry. Scribbling in my journal, I entitled the poem "Brotherhood."

> Christmas is the joy of giving
> Others bliss of expectation.
> Human ties of purple weaving
> Thread 'round our hearts in convocation.
> For our love is like a flame,

Burning bright, flickering low,
Yet always there; and it came
From Christ the Child whom we seek to know.

I paused in my writing, almost stunned by the sudden realization. Christ had laid aside everything to come to our dust and walk our planet. It wasn't new information. But it was becoming a heart realization in a deeper way. The King of glory had come for *me*. He'd left the throne in glory for a manger in a stinky sheep stable, all for the sake of love. I basked in the glow of this thought, thanking Him, loving Him. And then I thought again of the troubles we often face in human relationships. How small and mean we were! How much we needed His redemption!

All the following summer, I read and studied and prepared. I had discovered my passion in teaching that first year, and I wanted to be the best I could be. I had learned a lot about what worked and what didn't work with students, and the second year I felt more prepared and yet less confident in my own abilities. I felt more reliant on the Lord and prayer as I entered the classroom for another term of school.

Out of that second year of growth, I developed a teacher's creed to replace my lofty-sounding, vague teacher's pledge. It was a foundation upon which all my following years of teaching were built. I framed a copy and kept it where I could read it often.

I believe in a school that promotes the practices of a risen Saviour.

I believe that every attitude and condition of my heart should seek first the will of God and then let the heart ask, will it affect my students' attitude toward spiritual concepts; for perhaps my attitude will be theirs in later years.

I believe in an atmosphere of calm serenity in the schoolroom, even though I fall short of always catching hold of this mystifying and elusive temperament.

I believe in, and love, the sound of happy children playing outside; their faces alight with fun, the fun of being alive and loved. For I do love them very much, and know instantly when something is amiss in their lives.

I believe in the parents of my pupils. I know they overlook my mistakes and then trust me not to make the same ones repeatedly.

I believe in having a devotional period every morning. This begins the day with God, and a day begun with God must not go wrong.

I believe that I must lift up a standard so that the image of Jesus would be clear-cut and vivid at all times. My own petty ideas and frustrations must be left at home, for they are not welcome at school.

I believe that I am here to teach children scholastically and academically, helping them with math problems, English grammar, and historical facts; but if they learn nothing else, above all I would have them learn of Jesus.

CHAPTER 17

ADVENTURERS ABROAD

Her sleek black and red prow rose grandly out of the waters of the Atlantic. Her pristine decks and rails stood out white against the smoggy gray of the overcast New York sky. The *Queen Elizabeth II* was about to set sail, with us aboard. Our port of destination was Cherbourg, France.

It was the humid, foggy evening of June 13, 1975. I was twenty-six years old. Lena, JoAnn, and I with our sparse luggage, two 50-pound respirators and my wheelchair, had just set out on the grandest adventure we'd dreamed up yet. Dad had been afraid to let me go, I could tell. But he'd said yes.

With Dad's permission and growing excitement, the past several months had been spent in intense planning of every detail. I had commenced the laborious undertaking of phone calls and mapping out our tour. With the help of Flying Wheels Tours, a travel agency that specialized in arranging trips for people with disabilities, I was able to get the help I needed to make our plans concrete and doable.

A heavy, moist breeze ruffled my hair, wet against my cheek. I looked out over the vast expanse of the Atlantic, fog rolling in, and suddenly felt overwhelmed. Exhaustion and nausea washed over me. "I'm afraid I'm going to be sick, Lena."

"Let's go down to our stateroom. You can lie down and rest a little while," Lena consoled worriedly.

After a short while in my bunk, I felt improved enough to go on deck again. It was after 9:00 and twilight hung over everything. The glitter of city lights along the horizon cut through the light fog. We glided past Staten Island.

Then above us rose the Statue of Liberty. I leaned against the rail for support and looked at Lena thoughtfully. "This brings back the lines of poetry that always ring through my mind when I see pictures of the Statue."

"Wasn't it a gift from France to the U. S.?" JoAnn asked.

"Yes, the sculptor was Auguste Bartholdi."

"Oh, I thought that was Gustave Eiffel," Lena mused.

"He was the one who undertook the engineering process of putting her back together here in the U.S., right?" JoAnn remembered. "But what were your lines of poetry, Vera?"

The velvet gray of the night air slid by us, and the light of the uplifted torch in the silent statue's hand blazed out against the falling dark.

"Ah, yes. The poem was written by Emma Lazarus. It's called 'The New Colossus.' "

Taking a breath of sultry air, I began in short spurts to recite the grand poetry that sang like music to my ears.

> Not like the brazen giant of Greek fame,
> With conquering limbs astride from land to land;
> Here at our sea-washed, sunset gates shall stand
> A mighty woman with a torch whose flame
> Is imprisoned lightning, and her name
> Mother of Exiles. From her beacon-hand
> Glows world-wide welcome; her mild eyes command
> The air-bridged harbor that twin cities frame.

> "Keep, ancient lands, your storied pomp!" cries she
> With silent lips. "Give me your tired, your poor,
> Your huddled masses yearning to breathe free,
> The wretched refuse of your teeming shore.
> Send these, the homeless, tempest-tossed to me,
> I lift my lamp beside the golden door!"

"Ah, beautiful," Lena breathed. "I lift my lamp beside the golden door."

"But it's getting late." Lena turned to me. "We should have plenty of time to rest over the next four days of the voyage, but you weren't feeling well earlier, and I don't want you sick on this trip, Vera."

"You're right. It's so lovely out here, but we should go to bed, I suppose," JoAnn agreed.

I took a last, lingering look at that upraised torch slipping farther and farther away in the darkness, and the words of Jesus came back to me with startling clarity. "Let your light so shine before men . . ." *True liberty can come only from knowing Christ,* I mused. Those last words sounded so like His call to all who were weary, lost, lonely, and sick with sin.

> "Give me your tired, your poor,
> Your huddled masses yearning to breathe free,
> The wretched refuse of your teeming shore.
> Send these, the homeless, tempest-tossed to me,
> I lift my lamp beside the golden door!"

I could picture Him raising His lamp of truth as He stood beside the golden door of heaven, calling all the weary wanderers to Himself. I too was called to this light-bearing work. "Make us shine brightly, Lord," I whispered into the dark.

"Excuse me, ladies. May I ask you a question?" We turned from our stroll on the sunlit deck to see a portly, well-dressed gentleman.

I smiled at him and Lena responded, "You certainly can, sir. What is your question?"

"Well, I've been watching you all morning, and I was just curious to know what those cute little hats are on your head. Do they symbolize something, or are they just a style?"

Lena and I exchanged glances and her eyes twinkled as if to say, "Here's another opportunity."

"That's a good question. We get asked that question often. These are what we call coverings, and we wear them because we are Mennonite Christians who want to practice the Bible literally."

"How interesting! I've heard of Amish before. Are the Mennonites the same thing as Amish?"

"Well . . ." Lena paused and searched for the right words. "We are similar in many ways. We have a lot of the same practices and beliefs, although there are some differences as well."

"I think it's very nice that you can practice your faith in this way. I admire people who live simply and are willing to be different for what they believe. But now I'm keeping you from your morning stroll. Thanks for taking time." He tipped his hat, smiled, and ambled away in the opposite direction.

"More curious than anything, I think," JoAnn said to me quietly.

"Perhaps you are right. But he seemed sincere," I parried.

The voyage held various opportunities to share our faith and heritage with a number of curious questioners. One older woman looked up "Mennonites" in the encyclopedia set in the ship's library. She found us later in the dining room and gushed, "Who would have thought? You're even in the *World Book Encyclopedia.* I thought I'd just look it up and right there on the page was a whole little write-up about you and your people. Isn't that just amazing?"

We nodded politely but had to smile at her surprise.

Our assigned table-mates in the dining room were a Dr. Garrett and his wife and two children. They were a high-class family who were willing to guide us through the intricacies of high-style dining and society. We quickly became friends, holding conversations on a host of various subjects over the exotic meals that were served three times a day. Toward the end of our ocean crossing, they donated three empty wine bottles to us for a project we had been talking about the day before.

Back in our room we found small scraps of paper and wrote John 3:16 on them, along with our names and addresses. Then we rolled them up, stuck them in the narrow mouths of the bottles, and corked them tightly. "Now for the launching of our message in a bottle," Lena announced dramatically. Standing at the rear of the ship, we each took turns tossing our bottles overboard and watching them get lost in the dark waves below. When it was my turn, I had to ask Lena to help me. Unobtrusively, so as to make my arm appear as normal as possible, she grasped my elbow and propelled my arm over the railing. I let the bottle go, watching with satisfaction as it joined the others bobbing in the waves.

"I doubt anyone will ever find them, but it feels significant to have done it, anyway." JoAnn turned restlessly away from the rail. "Now if I can just finish out this cruise without that Italian horn player approaching me one more time, I'll call it a successful voyage."

Lena and I giggled. "He does seem quite eager to make your acquaintance," Lena said drolly. "Don't worry, JoAnn. It'll be a very short-lived attraction. Maybe Vera just needs to use her glare on him."

"That would scare him away," JoAnn agreed heartily. "Don't you think it's your sisterly duty to protect me, Vera?"

We all laughed together. It was Monday afternoon and our scheduled arrival in France was the next day. We were all feeling ready for the adventures that lay ahead. But as usual, there would be far more adventure than any of us had anticipated!

The next day our ship was greeted in harbor by a group of schoolchildren singing in French. Everywhere around me the lovely, poetic language that I'd struggled to master in high school flowed like water. Lyrical, lilting, laughing sounds—words that I knew, and yet the conversations were too quick and complex for me to follow.

I felt dazed by the mad rush of people around us. Everyone seemed to know where they were going and to be in a hurry to get there. Very few people made eye contact and even fewer of them smiled. The women especially seemed cold and harried. In the midst of the chaos and bustle of the disembarking passengers, with the noise and rush swirling around us, Lena stopped to pull out our itinerary.

"I feel lost," JoAnn sighed. "Just look at all these people."

"Where are we supposed to go for the night?" I asked anxiously.

"Well, first we have to find our car rental agency," Lena said, sounding stressed.

An English-speaking French couple from the ship came up behind us at that moment and noticed our plight. "Can we help you find something?" the silver-haired gentleman graciously asked.

"Oh, yes, sir! We need to find our car rental agency and a hotel for the night, and we are feeling rather confused at the moment as to where to go," Lena exclaimed with gratitude.

"Let me see your itinerary. What is the name of your car rental agency? Ah, yes. This place is located very near the docks here. Let us show you the way." Within a short time they had located the place for us and pointed out a nearby reputable hotel and restaurant as well.

"Thank you so much! I don't know what we would have done without your help!" I said as they turned to leave.

"Our pleasure. Safe travels!"

Our rental car was an orange Renault 12. "It's such a cheerful color," Lena commented. "Even if we get lost, others will know where we are, I guess." We all giggled in a stressed sort of way and loaded ourselves into the brilliant-colored vehicle that was to be our chariot for some days to come.

Upon arriving at our hotel and checking in, another crisis arose almost immediately.

"Vera! I don't know what we are going to do! Your electrical plug for your respirator won't fit in the outlet." Worry sharpened Lena's tone.

"Are you sure?" I asked anxiously.

"Positive. See?"

"Oh, no!" JoAnn groaned. "What are we going to do now?"

"I can't breathe at night without it." I failed to keep the panic out of my voice. "You have to do something, Lena. Do something quick."

"I don't know what to do," Lena moaned.

"I'm calling home," I declared. I was on the verge of tears. JoAnn quickly dialed the number for me, but my call went through to a French operator and I couldn't communicate well enough in French to get through. Finally I hung up in frustration. "Lena, we have to do something." I was crying now.

"I'll go down and ask at the front desk. Maybe they'll be able to help us," she assured me. "JoAnn, you stay here with Vera. I'll be right back. And while I'm gone, you'd better pray!"

We did pray, and she was back shortly with a handful of adapters to try. "One of these ought to work," she declared optimistically. The first two didn't, but the third one was the answer to our prayers. We shrieked with joy when the electric plug slid smoothly into the adapter.

"Thank God!" I exclaimed fervently.

"That was close," Lena agreed soberly.

We toured Paris a bit the next day. Lena's postcard home to our family described our collective feelings about the capital of France. "Paris was too fast for country girls! It didn't take us long to get out!"

We drove southeast to Lyon, which was a World Heritage Site. After viewing several of the popular historical and architectural landmarks and falling in love with the delightfully soft freshness of French bread, we drove the ninety-nine miles northeast to Geneva, Switzerland. We had strayed considerably from our original itinerary, but there seemed to be very little in France to hold us. Switzerland proved otherwise.

"Lena, look at the mountains! They are everything I dreamed they would be!" The Swiss Alps rose around us, towering majestically against a blue dome of sky. Their jagged, snow-capped peaks seemed to pierce heaven. The air here was clear and cool. The rolling meadows of mountain flowers nodded vivid and fresh, rolling away into the very hearts of those great fortresses of rock.

The old-fashioned chalets charmed us. We found the people welcoming and the traditional culture rich and full of history.

"It makes me think of the classic *Heidi*," JoAnn observed enthusiastically. "I can almost feel the story unfolding around us."

A traditional breakfast awaited us each morning at our hotel before we moved on for the day. For an easy-to-pack lunch, we enjoyed bread and fresh fruit, but that meant we were usually quite hungry by the time we found our ethnic restaurant of choice each evening.

In the bustling, history-rich city of Zurich, spread out in a valley and surrounded by towering Alps, we visited the Limmat River. As I watched the water move swiftly past us, I pondered history. This was the site of the martyrdom of the Anabaptist leader Felix Manz.

"I can almost see him standing here," I confided to Lena in a hushed voice. "Almost hear his voice come echoing down the ages to us."

"Like a call to be faithful to our heritage," Lena finished intuitively.

"It makes it seem so much more real somehow," JoAnn added.

And in my mind's eye I saw him standing there on the bank of the river, the sod of Switzerland solid beneath his feet. I could imagine the ropes that bound his wrists. They had cut and chafed him, but he seemed unaware of all of this. His eyes were raised to the overcast sky, but they seemed to see something beyond it.

Now he was being rowed to the middle of the river. The priest was asking him questions. But he only shook his head. I could see his mother and brothers and friends clustered on the shore watching with tense sorrow as their courageous fellow believer was shoved into the icy water. He was doomed to die as a heretic. But his last words had rung out triumphant and unafraid: "Into your hands, O Lord, I commend my spirit."

His physical life had been snuffed out that day, but his legacy and faith had lived on in the hearts of those who followed his example and witnessed his testimony that day. "The men and women like Felix who stayed true to Christ until death gave us a lasting legacy of faithfulness," I mused aloud. I was deeply challenged and stirred as we left. *Lord, let me be faithful to you,* I prayed in my heart, *like Felix was. Courageously and until death.*

That first Sunday in Europe we attended morning worship in our family's ancestral home town of Oberhofen. The following day we crossed the border into Germany and headed north toward Stuttgart.

We were driving through the famed Black Forest of Germany. Mountain ranges covered with rich, deep green forests hid rushing mountain streams and quaint houses hidden in quiet nooks.

As we drove, the sky darkened. We heard thunder rolling in the distance, and then the rain began to fall. Lightning flashed dangerously close, and thunder echoed against the mountains. Wind picked up and slashed the rain against our windshield and the trees overhead. Our headlight's beams seemed weak as they fought against the darkness of the driving storm.

Suddenly, without warning, our engine coughed and died. "Oh, no!" Lena groaned. "Not now! We're in the middle of nowhere!"

"Try restarting it," I urged.

The engine muttered but would not start. Repeatedly Lena turned the key in the ignition. From the backseat JoAnn gave ideas. "I'll have to get out and look under the hood," Lena decided bravely.

An hour later we still sat there, alone, stranded, and the car would not start. Lena had tried everything she knew. With tears standing in her brown eyes and rain dripping from her soaked hair, she looked at us pleadingly. "I just don't know what to do."

Helplessness seeped over us. We were in a foreign country. We were alone with no one to help and no one waiting for us tonight. We had no way to call anyone and no mechanical knowledge that seemed of any use. Dusk had begun to fall outside our rain-spattered windows. Frantic and on the verge of terrified, I said, "Lena, we've got to pray hard. It's our only hope."

"Lord, you see how much we need you. Please help this car to start." In turn we each pleaded with our heavenly Father to intervene on our behalf and reaffirmed our trust in His provision and protection. When JoAnn said "Amen," Lena turned the key once more and the engine roared to life. "Oh, thank you, Lord!" we all exclaimed together. With prayers and songs of thanks and relief in our hearts, we drove to the next town to spend the night.

At the border of East Germany we encountered communist guards at Checkpoint Charlie. They opened our trunk to survey its contents. They were polite and friendly and waved us through with little more than a teasing smile and a comment of "very nice faces" through the open car window.

In Berlin we had planned a weekend with Jimmy Miller, a brother to our brother-in-law Johnny. He was working as a missionary in the Mennonite congregation of Friedensheim and had promised to take us around to see the sites of the famous German city.

Soon we were hopelessly lost. We could not seem to find Friedensheim no matter where we turned. We asked person after person for help. Our Pennsylvania Dutch seemed of little use, and no one had heard of Friedensheim. With mounting urgency we felt relief wash through us when we saw a policeman in uniform. "Surely he'll help us," I declared confidently.

But when Lena approached him, he acted aloof and didn't seem to understand her very well. Near breaking point, Lena stamped her foot in frustration. "You must help us!" she demanded desperately in Pennsylvania Dutch.

The burly German officer looked at her sharply. He tried to hide a smile, but the corners of his mouth twitched in amusement and his eyes were laughing at us. At least we had his full attention now. Lena made one final desperate effort to explain our plight.

Just then a man walked up behind us. "I'll take you to Friedensheim. Just follow me. This way, girls." In dazed disbelief, we obeyed.

He drove ahead of us, leading us into a little cul-de-sac. As we parked our car and piled out to thank him, we watched, stupefied, as the car sped away and disappeared. "Could that have been an angel?" Lena voiced the question for all of us. Soon Jimmy was welcoming us warmly, and after we were settled in we told him the whole story. He was as mystified as we were as to who would have helped us and left without saying goodbye. When we parted to sleep for the night, we could only conclude that once again God had miraculously provided for us in a moment of need.

With Jimmy as guide, we spent the next several days shopping and sightseeing.

We met the congregation he was a part of and were blessed by their warmth and sincerity. One night we decided to join other Berliners in a common city pastime. With a dozen Freidensheim youth from his church, Jimmy accompanied us to a large city park. It was a warm, moonlit night, and with Jimmy pushing my wheelchair and the other youth spread out in front and behind, I felt secure and relaxed.

The park was large and the paths spacious. We talked, laughed, and sang hymns as we strolled along in the soft moonlight. Abruptly our path was blocked by the dark figure of a man who had stepped from the shadows beside the path.

He was dressed in civilian clothing and appeared to be neither a tramp nor a policeman, the only two types of people we would have expected to accost us. "Stop singing," he demanded. His voice was cold, commanding, tinged with hate. The night air seemed to be the only thing that breathed. All else was still. Waiting.

Looking at our silent, shocked group, he pulled a pistol from his belt. I seemed to be seeing the scene before me in slow motion. His hands moved in the shadows. Moonlight glinted off the black barrel of the gun. Jimmy had stepped out ahead of the rest of us when the man first accosted us. Now the man pointed the gun at Jimmy's stomach. I saw Jimmy's face twitch. I waited for the shot I was sure would come. It felt like a slow-moving nightmare.

"I mean what I said." The man's words were quiet and sinister. The hair on the back of my neck stood on end. He stepped to the side of the path and motioned us past. As if in a dream, we moved obediently forward, filing along the path past him. I waited for a shot in the back. It never came. But as the last person passed him and we picked up our pace, the voice came again through the darkness. "Remember what I said to you." His words were slightly slurred. "Don't come back this way either, or you'll be sorry."

Almost running, we put a safe distance between ourselves and the man before we dared to speak to one another. Then it seemed we were all talking at once. Everyone was shaken. When we reached a well-lit area of the park, Jimmy stopped the group. "Let's kneel down here and thank God for sparing us," he said fervently.

After thanking the Lord, we found another route and returned home as quickly as possible. The joy had disappeared from the walk, and all we wanted was to be safe inside. Once again God had proven His faithfulness through miraculous protection.

After making a brief stop in Holland, we left our rented orange chariot behind and boarded a flight for London on the third of July. There we spent almost a week touring the famed city where so much literary and historical interest was generated. I was delighted to be able to picture David Copperfield's smoggy London streets and Oliver Twist's back alleys. Twain's *The Prince and the Pauper,* Swift's *Gulliver's Travels,* and Chaucer's *Canterbury Tales,* along with a score of other fictional and biographical works I had read over time, came alive in new ways as I pictured scenes from their pages here in their actual setting.

After five days in England, we boarded our flight for New York, weary, worldly-wise, and full of memories and stories to tell. I couldn't wait to get home now. I had so many things I looked forward to sharing with my students in the coming school year, but first I needed to rest and recover from all our adventures.

CHAPTER 18

THE PILOT AND THE DYNAMITE

It was a cold, blustery day in mid-winter. All morning my students had been restless, and I could tell they needed a diversion. In the middle of the second class, I hit upon an announcement to motivate them to good behavior. "If you work extra hard, we'll have an early recess—and we'll all dress for the weather and go sledding," I offered.

An eager hand shot up from the back of the room. "Will you go with us, Sister Vera?"

"Yes, I will." I smiled at their motivation as they all bent over their work with renewed gusto. An hour later we were dressing up for the outdoors.

"You look like a teddy bear in all those wraps and that furry hood," my co-teacher Esther Smith grinned.

"Help me tie this scarf and then I'll be ready to go. Are you ready to ride down that hill, Esther? It will be nice and icy today." My eyes twinkled with fun.

"Sure, Vera, I'm ready. As I always say, you're the brain and I'm the hands.

You open the door and I'll follow."

"Now if you could just give me wings," I laughed.

"Oh, don't start that again." Esther blushed a little under her blue woolen scarf. "I'm really not a pilot, Vera. I just fly a small private plane for recreation."

"You are a pilot. A pilot is someone who flies a plane, isn't it?" I insisted. "That is the first thing I ever talked to you about. Remember when I stopped beside you and asked if you were the one who flew?"

"I do, indeed." Esther's wide blue eyes lighted with the memory. "I was embarrassed about it and there you were blurting it out in public as if it were some grand accomplishment."

"It is," I laughed. "And what was your first impression of me?"

"I wondered how so much dynamite could be packed into someone of such small stature." We giggled together like schoolgirls and went out into the snow. I was reaching my mid-thirties, and schoolteaching continued to be fulfilling for me, giving me a real sense of purpose and accomplishment in my life. It was made even more pleasurable when I had someone like Esther as a co-worker.

At the top of the hill the children were waiting for us. "Sister Vera! Sister Vera, over here is the best sled!" Several boys had selected a long, wooden toboggan for our ride.

Esther got on first, and I got on in front of her. Wrapping her arms tightly around me, she called, "Ready," and three or four little boys pushed us from behind. It was a giant shove, and with the rain that had fallen the day before, icing the snow, the sled rushed away in a flying sweep down the hill.

The biting cold wind blew strong in our faces. I laughed aloud with sheer enjoyment. I loved these moments when the wind confirmed that my paralyzed body was moving and I was embracing life. "Isn't this fun?" Esther laughed.

There was a large maple toward the bottom of the hill. As we came to a curve in the sledding path, Esther tried to steer around it, but the icy hill was too slick and the sled made straight for that tree trunk. "AHH! We're going to hit that tree!" I screamed. Solid, it loomed up before us.

"I'm going to bail!" Esther yelled in panic. Thinking quickly, she tightened her arms around me, pulling me to her chest and pressing her chin into my shoulder to pin me in even better. Then throwing her body weight off the sled a second before the sled hit the tree, she rolled with me in her grip into a big snow drift.

"You okay, Vera?" Esther let me go and peered at me anxiously.

"I think so. Are you okay?" The scarf had kept snow from getting in my mouth, but my hood was full of it. I rolled over and sat up.

"You look like a little snowman!" Esther giggled.

"You look like a pilot, crashed in a pile of snow," I quipped back.

"Some pilot. I can't even steer a sled." Esther shook her head in mock disgust, and I burst into peals of laughter. She joined me and we laughed until our sides ached in hilarity and relief.

Back in the classroom that afternoon, my students seemed more settled after the outdoor exercise. History class was the first afternoon class, and I noticed with relief that one of my upper grade boys seemed to be taking a new interest in his history lesson. It had been a struggle for some time to get him to engage and learn, and I had been searching for ways to help him.

About halfway through class, I decided to quiz him on some of the dates I had asked them to memorize from the Early Renaissance period we were studying. I wanted to reward him for his diligence with a chance to share what he was learning. He looked sheepish when I called his name, and when he came reluctantly up to my desk, I second-guessed my decision.

When he laid his open book on my desk I saw what had been fascinating him. It was a sports magazine that fit perfectly between the pages of the large history text. My heart sank. Looking up at him with a mixture of severity and disappointment, I said nothing for a moment. His eyes met mine briefly and then shifted away. He shuffled his feet and his face turned red.

"Why did you do this?" I asked quietly.

"Dunno," he mumbled. "I'm sorry." Beads of sweat were forming on his forehead, and his hands were shaking. Though he was three times my size, I could tell he was afraid.

"Please look at me." He did and there was sorrow in his gaze, mingled with shame. He regretted having disappointed me, and I could tell he was sorry.

"We'll talk about this after school. You may leave the magazine on my desk and return to your seat."

I kept the punishment light and tried to fit it to the crime. This was one of my greatest challenges as a teacher, to balance all the relational aspects of my profession. I wanted to understand and befriend each of my students, but I was also aware that respect and consequences were crucial to good teaching.

Later as Esther and I discussed the day before going home, I confided, "Sometimes I find it such a challenge to know what the right decision is, you know? That's why I started having the students pray with me before I discipline them. You can tell a lot about how repentant children are if you hear them pray. And it gives me a chance to pray for them as well. It's really bonding."

"Oh, that's an excellent idea, Vera. I know what you mean. And the students highly respect you," Esther reassured me. "By the way, I have a parents' meeting later today. I wondered if you have any advice for me."

"Listen to them, Esther. That's the best thing you can do. If you listen to their frustrations and hear where they are coming from, they will feel your respect, and it will give you an opportunity to explain things without making them feel attacked. I like to ask the question, 'What do you think I should do in this situation? How would you like me to handle this?' They feel like they are on your team, and it gives them confidence that you are on theirs."

"I like that. That's good advice."

"Oh, and before I forget, what song would you recommend for my devotions tomorrow? We're reading from Romans 8 about being more than conquerors, and I was trying to remember that hymn you used in your classroom last week." Esther and I were constantly exchanging ideas, comparing notes, and sharing stories.

"Do you want to go out for breakfast on Monday morning?" I asked.

"Sure, but we'll have to get up early."

"I'll be ready for you at the crack of dawn." I laughed and we parted ways.

Monday morning was drizzly, and dawn hadn't broken yet when Esther picked me up. We headed for the town of Alliance.

"Country Manor is where you wanted to go, right?" Esther asked.

"Yes. It will be lovely to eat a hot breakfast together before school." I leaned back in the seat happily, envisioning our cozy time, lulled by the engine and the warmth from the heater vents. Conversation was sporadic. We'd both wake up more after we'd had our coffee.

As we were sitting in the turning lane with our blinker on, we planned what we'd order off the menu. "I think I want bacon this morning and maybe—" My sentence was cut off by a horrific *CRASH,* accompanied by a jarring thud.

I felt myself flying through the air. My body crashed into the dash and bounced off into Esther's lap.

For a dazed moment all was still. I felt as if I might suffocate in my present position, and I could see very little. "Pick me up!" I shrieked. "Pick me up!" I caught sight of Esther. She looked dazed. She would tell me later that when the car hit us, her neck snapped back and then bounced forward from the impact, smashing her head against the window and knocking her momentarily unconscious.

In a panic I yelled, "Put me back on the seat. Let's go. Get this thing going!" I wasn't thinking. I was just desperate to get off the road.

"Vera, we've been in an accident. We can't just go." Esther's voice was trembling. Shakily, she reached out and set me on my seat, where I started to realize how irrational I had sounded when I demanded that we get going. "We have to wait," Esther repeated. "The rear end is smashed in."

"I know . . ." I sighed in a small voice.

A policeman soon arrived on the scene. The driver who had crashed into us was a teacher who had been on her way to an early breakfast at the same restaurant with a co-teacher. She had been so busy visiting that she hadn't seen us in time to stop. We exchanged insurance information, and by that time Esther's calm strength had taken over, despite her pain.

"We'll have to skip breakfast, I guess. We'll be a bit late getting back as it is," she decided. I agreed, and we headed for the school.

"I think I'm going to need some painkillers to make it through the day," I told her.

"Me too." She grinned at me ruefully. "At least we aren't dead."

By the time we got to our classrooms, we were bruised, hungry, shaken, and late. Our whole day felt off, and we took painkillers multiple times. Eventually Esther learned that she had ruptured a disk in her neck. We both would have been wise to visit the hospital after an accident like that, but we were young and determined. And we didn't miss that day of class, even for an accident.

Esther and I not only shared the classroom, but all of life as well. We read and dialogued about endless books and subjects, often reading the same book and then comparing notes. When we weren't planning another field trip or discussing classroom issues, we often shared spiritual insights and stories from our childhoods. We taught together for five years, and in those years a deep bond was forged that would last a lifetime.

One of our most unforgettable adventures together outside the classroom happened on a snowy Saturday afternoon. We had gone out for a drive together. One of my favorite things was driving in pristine, untouched snow. "Look at the beauty, Esther. Look at the vast whiteness. It's like a snow sculptor came down and took up residence here."

Esther sighed happily. "Isn't it lovely? I love snow when the sun sparkles on it. Its whiteness always makes me think of Christ washing our hearts clean and pure."

The drifts were deep and the day was cold, but inside the warm car we purred along for over an hour. When we came upon a little back road that cut between Buffalo Road and Knox School Road, I saw that the world of snow was even more deep and beautiful down its mysterious-looking corridor.

"Turn down there, Esther," I directed.

"It hasn't been plowed out. We'll get stuck," Esther protested practically.

But I was undaunted. Perhaps it was because I had fought limitations all my life. Or maybe it was just because of my innate stubbornness, but I insisted that she turn down that road despite her inhibitions. Finally she gave in.

"Give it plenty of gas and you'll be fine," I said confidently. "Oh, aren't you glad we came this way? Look at that beauty!"

"It is lovely." Esther's voice had an edge in it, and I could tell she was nervous. We crossed a darling little bridge. Heaps of whiteness snuggled up to the road. A white track of unbroken snow lay before us. At the end of the road the snow looked deeper. "Give it the gas," I urged. I didn't want us to get stuck when we'd almost made it to the end of the road.

With good grace Esther stepped on the accelerator and the big Buick Electra surged ahead, straight into a huge mound of snow. The snow was so deep it churned up over the hood of the car.

"Give it the gas, Esther!" I yelled eagerly. "Give it more gas!"

But this time all my optimism and urging got us nowhere.

"Look, Vera. We're stuck." Esther's voice was patient but disgruntled.

I looked around and realized that there was snow up to our windows all around us and that we were indeed stuck.

"So I don't suppose there's any way to open the door and get out of here?" I asked slowly.

"No. The doors won't open. Look, the snow is up to the windows."

"Okay. Well, is there anything we *can* do?" I asked, trying to be practical.

Esther was silent for a moment. "I can't work miracles. I think we'll just have to be patient and wait for help to come."

We lapsed into silence. I prayed that God would send someone to get us out. Shortly, someone saw our plight and came tramping and puffing through the deep snow with a shovel. Our Good Samaritan was Harley Hilliard, Esther's neighbor. As he shoveled that deep, sticky snow away from our car, his face turned red with exertion.

"I hope he doesn't get a heart attack from all that hard work," Esther commented worriedly. "I know he has to be careful of his heart."

"Let's pray that he'll be all right," I said, my brows furrowing with concern. I saw the folly of my idea now and felt regret.

When we were finally shoveled out, we thanked Harley profusely and made our way toward home. "See? I can't perform miracles, Vera." Esther looked over at me and her eyes twinkled. "Even if I am a pilot."

"I guess I just thought you could do anything," I grinned sheepishly. "Let's go home and have a hot cup of coffee."

CHAPTER 19

MY DREAM

Every year I taught, I learned more about what I believed and how to help students. I learned what worked and what didn't. One of the greatest lessons I learned was that often beneath behavioral issues lurked hidden pain. Not all my students were church children. Some of them came from the community. Sometimes they came from abusive homes. I often reminded myself to be extra careful and watchful for these children who had never experienced the safety and love of a healthy home. And no matter what issues I faced with my students, I learned that understanding, communication, and affirmation were the biggest keys to their hearts.

One day a fifth grade boy in my class was acting up. He was one of my more difficult students, but today he was much more aggressive and naughty than usual. Calling him up to my desk during recess, I asked him, "What's wrong? You usually don't act like this."

He looked away from me for a long moment and then with tears in his eyes he admitted, "This morning my dad drowned my puppies."

"Oh, how terrible. I'm so sorry. But why did he drown them?"

"Because they were mutts." He was crying now, and I put out my hand to comfort him.

"I'm so sorry," I repeated with feeling. We sat in silence for a little while, and then he looked at me with hope in his dark eyes.

"Do you think dogs go to heaven?" he asked. "Because if they did, my puppies would be in heaven."

I prayed for wisdom, pausing for a long moment. Then I told him that I didn't know the answer to his question, but I reassured him that God did care about how he felt. We talked for a while about loss and sorrow and the choice to forgive. When we had finished, he gave me a shy smile and went out to play with his classmates. My heart ached for him, and I prayed that he wouldn't let this incident harden his heart.

Other students needed a firm hand rather than sympathy. There were two brothers who came to my class for a time. The younger one was more competitive and academically accomplished. The older brother had a learning disability and struggled with inferiority and anger. He'd attended public school before he came to our school. There he'd been mocked and bullied. Now he seemed to have given in to self-pity as well. I felt that no matter what I tried, I couldn't motivate him.

Things came to a crisis one day when he had a run-in with another student during recess. When I called him into the classroom to talk, he slouched in. He had often been honest with me about his life and problems, and I cared about him deeply, but I realized he needed to grow up and be a man. Praying inwardly for wisdom, I asked him to look me in the eye and listen to what I had to say. Sheepishly, he complied.

"Do you think I enjoy my limitations? Do you think I've never wanted to run and enjoy all the freedoms a normal person enjoys?"

He shrugged. "I don't know, Sister Vera."

"Of course I have, Jim. I miss doing those things every day. But I have made a choice. That choice is to live with purpose despite the limitations God has allowed me to have."

"But I'm not smart like you, Sister Vera."

"Jim, stop whining and listen. You often complain that girls never like you because you are too tall, and that you can't learn because it's too hard. I'm tired of hearing that kind of self-pity. Is it helping you grow at all? Is it helping you succeed in school?"

"It's too hard." His voice had taken on a plaintive note.

"Every day, I have to fight to overcome my limitations. Every day I endure pain and difficulty. But do you think that is what I focus on?"

He shook his head. "No."

"Do you think God expects any less of you?"

"No."

"Jim, you have an incredible amount of ability and strength. You have a body that functions and a mind that can think. You were created for a purpose. Are you willing to allow God to help you try instead of giving in to self-pity? If you want to be a man, you have to take responsibility and do your best. You will be stronger for the odds you have to overcome."

His face was thoughtful. For a long moment he was silent. Then, looking up, he nodded and a slight smiled brushed his lips. "You're right, I guess. I never thought of that before. Thanks, Sister Vera. Will you pray for me?"

Together we prayed, and in the months to come I watched with joy as those prayers were answered. Jim became industrious and fought to overcome his challenges. As he grew in strength and confidence, his troubles with the other students tapered off as well.

Another day it was a student with vulgar language. Several things I insisted on were good manners, pure speech, and no mocking of others. When these boundaries were crossed, I was seen at my most severe. This time it was an upper grade boy. Without ceremony I told him to follow me to the bathroom.

By the time we reached our destination, I think fear had begun to grow in him. I gave him my proverbial glare and announced calmly, "You see that soap right there?"

"Yes, Sister Vera."

"I want you to take that bar of soap and clean your mouth out, please."

"Me, do it to myself?"

"I think you'd better if you don't want a visit to the principal's office," I reiterated boldly.

"Whatever you say," he stammered. Awkwardly he obeyed. When he had finished, we returned to the classroom.

"Life and death are in the power of the tongue," I reminded him. "God hears every word you say. Let this prove a lasting reminder and warning to watch your words in the future."

"Yes, Sister Vera." His words were meek and I could tell he was thoroughly chastened. I never heard him use bad language again.

In 1982 Philip Stoltzfus joined our school staff to accommodate a classroom adjustment. A classroom was added, and Philip taught grades six through nine while I taught grades three through five, and Esther took Room 1 with its first and second graders. I had met Philip years ago in Belize. He remained for eleven years of my teaching career and became not only a valued fellow teacher, but also a good friend. He treated me like a sister and always went out of his way to look out for my well-being at school. Conscientious, studious, and servant-hearted, he shoveled the sidewalks of snow, swept school halls, and even hung stray coats. When his father died of cancer, I admired his care for his mother.

One day soon after we had begun teaching together, the three of us teachers went out for a meal. "I admire the way you two seem to work so well as a team," Philip commented.

"Oh, we do work wonders together," I laughed. "Even if they are disastrous sometimes."

"Don't tell that story!" Esther groaned.

Somehow as we continued talking, an incident from my youth came up. "Lena and I realized we were going to be late for our curfew, and we had our black Comet at that time. Looking around, we decided the roads were nearly deserted. 'I'll go eighty and we might make it in time,' Lena had said anxiously.

"Speeding through the night, I watched the darkness slide by the windows and wondered how it would feel during daylight hours. I loved speed. 'We're still going to be late,' I had pointed out. 'Try going ninety.'

"Lena did, and with me watching for police lights out our back window, she pressed the pedal to the floor. When I looked back at the speedometer it was at one hundred. 'Lena, are you serious?' I laughed incredulously.

" 'I think we'll make it in time,' she responded lightly.

"Looking back on that now, I realize it was foolhardy—and we never did it again. But I still love speed."

"Tell the story about going past the church with Delilah driving," Esther said, grinning at me. "I don't think you're the only one who loves speed."

"Oh, that story," I laughed. "I always liked speed, but Delilah was the wild one with cars. That day Mom was sitting on the tailgate just like the demure lady she is. I was in the back of the truck with one of the other girls. We went around the church corner and without realizing that one of the church members was standing in the churchyard, Delilah squealed her tires quite loudly. The brother looked startled, but Mom raised her hand and waved as if nothing had happened and she was just out for a sunny drive. When we got back to the house, we girls laughed until our sides hurt."

"Vera, you have a high-spirited side that goes way beyond what we see in the classroom." Philip shook his head, chuckling. "I do see you admit your mistakes, though, when your ideas don't turn out to be the best."

At that, Esther chimed in, "We make lots of decisions and mistakes together, but forgiving each other makes it all come right in the end."

I never could bring myself to fail a student. When I encountered students with disabilities, I often spent after-school hours and summers tutoring them to help them catch up to the other students. Whenever I could, I purposefully chose things I knew they had mastered, and would call them up front to answer a question or work a problem on the board for class demonstration. The smile of triumph they always gave me when they'd finished was more than enough reward for all the hours behind the scenes.

My favorite teaching days of all were the special days, such as winter picnics up on the hill and kite days when varied kites in bright colors on the end of tightly wound string sailed away above the valley below. An endless array of pet days, girls' days, boys' days, and other special events enlivened our learning. On one pet day my niece Hannah brought a little piglet wrapped in a blanket. "His name is Chubby. I brought him because I know how much you like piglets."

"He's adorable," I gushed. We shared a special smile, and I stroked Chubby's silky ears.

Poetry days, when we sat on the hill with the wind in our hair and contemplated nature, were perhaps my favorite special days of all. For weeks I prepared them for the day. I read them poetry daily, and as a class we collaborated to write a poem of our own. When we had finished it, we discussed what parts flowed and how rhyme and meter work. We talked about choosing words for their beauty and how poetry touches the soul like prose rarely can. When we finished changing and editing our class poem to perfection, we had several other individual exercises.

On one poetry day late in October, my students felt the mounting excitement as we spilled out of the school into the crisp fall day. I felt a thrill go through me. Life was beautiful!

Taking my go-cart, I met my troop of a dozen merry third, fourth, and fifth graders at the top of the hill behind our farmhouse. It was known in the community as "The Hill," and it gave a sweeping view of the rolling valley below it. It was my favorite spot on the farm. Below us country roads wound away, and trees in burnished autumn coats stood drinking in the sun. The sky above us was vivid azure.

Reclining on a blanket on the ground, I watched my students with pleasure. Each one was undertaking the great goal of writing his first real poem, and every face was alive with concentration and study. Each one was so different, yet each one was such a gift.

I pondered how things had begun to change in my family as well. As the years passed, slowly nieces and nephews began to attend my class. For me this was a special extension of my life passion. Because I would never have children of my own, my nieces, nephews, and students became like my children. I loved how they confided in me and eagerly helped me with little tasks like taking food out of my lunch box and putting it in front of me so I could reach down and get it with my mouth.

Both Mom and Dad were aging. Most of my siblings were married now, yet our family was as close as ever in many ways. I thought back to the recent ordination of my sister Delilah's husband. She had stood crying at the sobriety and weight of the moment when Lena put her arms around her to comfort her. "Oh, Lilah, you will be just fine. You will make a wonderful bishop's wife. Quit crying."

I grinned as I remembered what followed in such typical Overholt sister fashion.

"Oh, hush! You know that's not true, Lena," Delilah had choked out quietly.

"Hush yourself! You know *that's* not true!" Lena had shot back with a smile in her voice.

They both had to restrain their laughter, and I laughed quietly with them. I felt so blessed to have such a wonderful family who were constantly involved in my life. Without their firm support both physically and emotionally, I wouldn't be able to teach.

"Sister Vera." I looked up to see one of my fourth graders, his dark eyes shining eagerly. "I finished my poem. Will you look at it?"

"Certainly." I took it and carefully read the words. He described the valley and the varied colors of the fall season. I smiled at the budding talent I saw in the simple phrases.

"Excellent work. I can see you put a lot of creative thought into it. Here are just a few suggestions for changes that could make it even better."

After he had corrected it, I read it once more and gave my student a warm smile. "Maybe someday you'll be an author." His shy grin was more than payment.

That afternoon in celebration of our finished poetic works, we played a game of baseball. As I sat watching and cheering for the players, it took me back to the article I had finished the week before for an issue of *News and Notes,* a local teachers' newspaper. I had entitled it "My Dream."

I suppose it is the dream of every teacher to produce students who develop into mature adults and respond in a healthy Christian way to situations. I began teaching with this dream, and, thank God, I still have it in a more real way than ever!

I can hardly believe that sixteen years have gone by since I entered the classroom that first scary September morning. These have been good years—years to learn patience among numerous other things which have helped to strengthen my spiritual life. I love working with my students, for they have eternal value! Nothing can give such personal satisfaction as doing work that you enjoy and doing work that is worthy.

Some mornings I can hardly wait to enter my quiet, clean classroom and set up some new project for the children, just to be able to watch the sparkle and gleam light up their intelligent eyes.

I had time to muse as I mingled with the youth while camping at Camp Peniel last weekend. Most of the youth were former students of mine. They were no longer children at school, but sensitive young people who were actively involved in their own lives; youth who were struggling not with math problems and history questions, but with life itself—that great and mighty question of life and its meaning!

I thanked God for their Christian background and spiritual teaching, resting assured that all would be well because of their inner desire to do right.

I was also encouraged and delighted by one small incident. As I was standing by the ball field, I felt a real kinship to each one there. The day was perfect, the air crisp and clear. The sky overhead was blue and the clouds floated lazily above us. Best of all, there was a beautiful camaraderie between counselors and everyone. No one had an age; we were one. About this time, someone rode up on my golf cart with ice water and I heard someone yell, "Hey, Vera, do you want some water?" Oh, I did! So one of my former pupils came graciously bearing a cold drink. Now I wondered if he would remember that I couldn't hold the glass to my lips. I didn't need to wonder. In true gentleman style, he offered the drink, casually chatting about the game. The sun shone a little brighter. The trees were a little bit greener. For truly my students were responding to the needs of others. My dream had come true!

CHAPTER 20

LIFE IS A GIFT

Summer had come again and school was out for the year. The light ripples on the pond caught the glint of afternoon sunlight and cottony clouds reflected in its dark water.

"It's a perfect day for fishing, isn't it, Aunt Vera?" John's boyish voice broke into my ponderings.

"Yes, perfectly beautiful. You couldn't have picked a better afternoon." I smiled approvingly at my nephew.

He held his pole steadily out over the water. "Maybe we'll catch fish for supper," he said hopefully.

"We just might," I agreed. I adjusted my toes around my own pole and tugged a little, watching my red and white bobber bounce on the water's surface.

All at once from behind us, a long, low bellow sounded. I looked around, startled. Coming around the corner of the field was Dad's herd of cows, and in the lead was the hulking, surly bull.

"He's pretty mad," John observed. "He's coming for the pond, Aunt Vera. Look!" His voice took on a note of alarm as the bull charged toward us. Only one strand of barbed wire stood between us and him.

Taking quick stock of the situation, I seized upon the picnic table nearby. "If we need to, we can go under the picnic table, John. But you'll have to help me," I planned.

The bull paused in his rampage a few yards from the fence, tossing his head, snorting, and pawing the ground. He breathed hard through his nose, and his red-rimmed eyes looked fearsome at such close range. He threw his head back and let out a long, roaring bellow, rolling his eyes as if in utter disgust and rage.

"We'd better get under that table now, John," I urged. My thought was cut short by the sound of Dad's big black truck. He came driving at high speed, bumping across the pasture. He must have seen what was happening, because he headed straight for that angry bull. As he often had throughout my life, my dad stepped in again and saved the day. Seeing the truck, the bull turned and trotted away, bellowing. Shaken but unhurt, John and I hitched a ride back to the farmhouse with Dad. Fishing was forgotten until another time.

Sharing life with my nieces and nephews was one of my greatest joys. One night in the churchyard I shared a secret adventure with my nephew Dwight. Dusk had fallen over everything, but we waited quietly for dark to creep in on velvet feet before we left our vehicle. "Aunt Vera, why are we waiting till after dark?" Dwight's small voice asked in a whisper at my elbow.

"Because it has to be a surprise for everyone," I explained softly.

My friend Jerry chuckled beside me. "That's right. It's the secret of the hour."

Judy was with us too, carrying more bulbs than the ones Jerry and Dwight already carried.

In the soft dirt, we dug holes and buried the daffodil bulbs by flashlight. "See, Dwight? This is how you do it. You plant the bulb in a hole three times as deep as the bulb itself. Tap the soil over it gently. You want to place the next bulb about six inches from the first one."

"Like this, Aunt Vera?"

"Yes, perfect."

That following spring when the bulbs grew up and blossomed in the church-yard, Dwight shared in the thrill of the success of our surprise enterprise. They would bloom for years to come.

⁓

When my second pet dog, a terrier, had passed away, I knew I needed another dog. My choice this time was a soft, black schnauzer. His bright black eyes and black button nose were framed by fluffy black fur. "You are a darling! I think I'll name you Hans," I told my new friend.

Hans quickly joined my adventurous life. The week after I got him, my friend Bruce and I had a typical trip planned to visit someone in the hospital. I planned to take my nephew John with us. When I thought of Grandma Snyder lying in the hospital, I knew I needed to take Hans along to visit her. She had lost her own dog recently, and I knew it would mean something to her. I had taken my students to visit several times, but this time I would bring her a special visitor!

"It will be just like Joni Eareckson Tada's story when her boyfriend smuggled a puppy in to see her," I planned with Bruce. "We'll put him in my pink bag and hide him until we are past the nurses' station. Just think how surprised Grandma Snyder will be!" Bruce's broad smile and hearty laugh expressed his full approval of my plan.

I had met Bruce at church as he attended occasionally. One thing I quickly discovered was that Bruce had a giant heart of gold. He was constantly visiting shut-ins, cooking meals for people, taking the down-and-out into his home, and sharing Christ with everyone he came in contact with. He and I hit it off and, with various others, were soon involved in impromptu ministry opportunities in our community.

Today he'd cooked a meal for Grandma Snyder. "She doesn't like the hospital food," he confided. "I thought it would do her heart good to have a home-cooked meal, you know."

"Of course, Bruce. You always think of such things."

"Aunt Vera, what if Hans barks?" little John asked from the back seat.

I laughed. "We'll pray he stays quiet," I said merrily.

"What if they say you can't have him in the hospital?" John seemed worried. His personality was sensitive and careful, and he was thinking ahead as usual.

"We won't get upset or offended. We'll just take him and leave if they ask us to," I reassured him confidently.

When we got to the hospital, Bruce took out my wheelchair, affectionately known as "Molly." It was a standing wheelchair that Dad had designed and welded just for me. Its pink and ivory padding made it quite attractive, and the pink bag attached to it was where we hid my furry black puppy.

I grinned at Bruce and he grinned back. We felt almost like naughty schoolchildren as little John, Bruce, and I sallied past the nurses' station, holding the puppy's head down inside the bag. We knew the number of Grandma's Snyder's room from former visits and went there directly.

"Hello!" Bruce greeted her with warmth. "We've brought some sunshine for you!"

"How wonderful!" she beamed. "Come right in. Come right in." Her silver hair framed a smile-wrinkled face and lively, intelligent eyes.

"We've brought you a special visitor today," I announced.

"Oh, it's John! So good to see you, son."

"No, Grandma Snyder, it's not me," John said shyly.

"Go ahead and get him, John," I smiled.

As John pulled the puppy from his hiding place, Grandma Snyder expressed joy and wonder, her face a brilliantly happy smile as she patted the bed eagerly. "Oh! Did you really? He's beautiful! Put him here."

Just then the nurse came in. We all looked up, surprised. "Oh, don't tell the head nurse," we begged together.

"It's a surprise for Grandma Snyder," John explained pleadingly.

"Of course not. I wouldn't think of it." The nurse smiled and patted Hans' head gently. "Is he a schnauzer?" she asked.

"Yes, isn't he lovely?"

"He sure is. I actually raise schnauzers. They are tremendous companions. I can't say enough good about them."

As she continued to chat with us, the head nurse came in. We all waited a bit tensely, but the kind woman acted blind to the puppy on the bed. She smiled at us, went about her business and left shortly after. When we had finished our visit and hugged Grandma Snyder goodbye, we snuggled Hans back into his little nest inside my pink bag and left the hospital, laughing.

My adventurous streak continued to extend to speed. A wild ride in a boat on the coast was a delightful memory from one summer. Later, however, the joy of boats came to an end after an accident I witnessed and barely escaped. I was visiting Olan and Lena in Georgia, and Larry Kauffman was giving Lena and me a careful ride one afternoon in his little boat. It had a very large motor for the size of the boat, and Olan had warned us about the danger of riding in it. When a teenage neighbor boy joined Larry on the boat, Lena and I decided it would be wise to get off.

Within moments of our evacuation, the men revved the motor a little too high and the boat flipped over. The motor cut off and the two men dove underneath. The boat flipped onto its side, and neither Larry nor the boy were hurt, but I felt as if I were watching a nightmare.

"Lena, if I had been on that boat, I would have drowned."

"I know, Vera. God was gracious," Lena agreed.

That night I couldn't sleep. The scene of the tipping boat went through my mind again and again. I thanked God for the gift of life and the gracious sparing of mine He had performed that day.

Another time I rode on a motorcycle with my sister and her boyfriend. I was tightly sandwiched between them because I had very little balance of my own to keep me on. I felt totally out of control. As soon as Cliff took off, I started to scream in fear. The ride was short-lived because of this terror. I decided I would never try a motorcycle ride again. But that was before I realized there was more than one way to ride.

It was at the Joni & Friends Family Retreat that I got another chance to ride. I had been going to these retreats for several years with my sisters, enjoying the seminars and fellowshipping with others who had life limitations in varying degrees. Christ-centered worship, practical seminars on family issues related to living with disabilities, and evenings filled with campfires and enjoyable group activities made these retreats the highlight of many summers for me.

Often I participated in the fundraisers for their overseas distribution of wheelchairs to impoverished people with disabilities. This included a walk-athon where a nephew would push my wheelchair the distance of the race. Businesses in our community donated generously, and I had the joy multiple times of sharing large sums with this incredible cause.

It was on an afternoon at one of the retreats that I got my motorcycle ride. They strapped my wheelchair, with me in it, onto a tiny trailer pulled by a motorcycle. The wind whipped against my face and ruffled my hair, and I laughed in sheer delight as the motor roared and the wheels spun over the tar. When we stopped, I blurted, "That was a good ride, but can I go again? It wasn't quite fast enough." Laughing, the driver heartily complied. The next ride was a ride to remember. Perfectly fast enough to fit my taste for speed!

As the years passed and my numerous nieces got older, they started taking me to the retreats in the place of my sisters. These days became great opportunities for bonding and growing together in our relationships. I couldn't have attended without their willing help and love.

Times with my nieces and nephews were always my most joy-filled hours, and this would extend to the next generation of nieces and nephews as well. One day two of my great-nieces came running to show me their pet baby chick.

Cuddling him against her cheek, Sylvia explained, "See, Aunt Vera, his leg is hurt. So we named him Crippy."

"Oh, you'll have to change his name," I countered quickly. "You should never refer to something according to its handicap."

"Why, Aunt Vera?" Kara's large brown eyes were solemn with question.

"Because it's seeing someone according to their looks instead of valuing them for their soul," I explained firmly. "You must always look in the heart to see the true beauty, Kara."

I taught this in my classroom as creatively as I could. I wanted each of my students to learn that handicaps were not what defined people, and that by being aware of how it felt to live with a disability, they could smooth the way for disadvantaged persons and graciously treat them with dignity.

On handicap day, I would assign each student a handicap. One would be on crutches while another had to spend the day with his arm in a sling. They always entered in with good grace and enjoyed many laughs through the blunders of their day.

"The other day in church someone tried to hand me a hymnbook," I shared on one handicap day. "They had forgotten I couldn't reach out for it. They apologized profusely, but I told them it was really a compliment. The greatest gift you can give someone who is asked to live with limitations is to simply treat them like a normal human being." Pausing, I added, "The greatest gift one friend ever gave me were the simple words, 'I don't care about your scar, Vera. I care about your heart.'

"Remember this when you relate to others, children. Even something as simple as stuttering can be very embarrassing for the person who struggles with it. Many people try to help someone finish his sentence when he stutters. But by simply looking at him calmly and waiting for him to finish as if nothing is wrong, we can give him the confidence he needs to tell us what is in his heart without fear. Just quietly wait. This gives him dignity."

I had learned to live with my limitations quite smoothly. I did my best to live a normal existence. I had found that the less I made of my disability, the more quickly others accepted it as insignificant. However, sometimes this hindered me from getting the help I needed. It made me stubborn toward change, sometimes to the detriment of both my body and the ease of those who helped with my care.

Soon after my forty-second birthday, I began to struggle increasingly with weakness and dizziness. I hated the phrase "post-polio respiratory weakness." I was certain that my chest cuirass, a ventilator that sat on top of my chest at night, was adequate, despite having heard speakers talk about the benefits of other breathing devices. I had family activities, church activities, teaching, travel, and friends to worry about. I didn't have time to worry about my health. Or so I thought.

When pumping my body with vitamins didn't seem to help, I visited our local physician. When he heard about my dizziness, he treated me for inner ear problems. Despite the lack of improvement from this treatment, I thought, *I'm simply getting older. I'll do better in the fall when it's cooler.* Being optimistic, I refused to admit that something more serious was going on.

A visit to the dentist produced such severe claustrophobia and dizziness that I had to leave the building. At night I dreaded brushing my teeth. Every time I did, I struggled to breathe. That fall as school started again, I would sometimes fall asleep at my desk while helping the children with their studies. They were gracious and would simply trot off and bring me a cup of coffee to wake me up. But I knew that something would have to be done.

"You have got to get help," my sisters insisted.

"Vera, you don't even realize how bad things have gotten," Lena pleaded with me. "You need to see a specialist." I finally gave in.

My answer came through a BiPAP system with a mask. Despite my insistence that I simply needed a better fitting cuirass, my specialist overrode my opinion. My phobia made me fearful of having a mask over my face, but he insisted I try it. The first time I put the mask on and felt the air begin to flow, I pulled it off in a panic. "I can't do this!" I declared. But in my heart of hearts, I knew better.

When I looked at the situation realistically, I realized it was either a tracheotomy or this. I didn't want the trach, so I set about to train myself to accept the mask. With tender help from my family, I learned to see the mask as a friend and eventually I began to look forward to putting it on at night.

With this adjustment in my health care plan, my horrible headaches disappeared along with my sleepiness, dizziness, and the swelling in my ankles. My body simply hadn't been getting enough oxygen to function. As zest for life and renewed energy returned, I once more thanked God for the gift of life.

CHAPTER 21

IN RETROSPECT

I brooded over my cup of coffee. Staring into the rich brown of my favorite drink, I caught the distorted reflection of my face peering back. Pensively restless, I looked out the window at the gray sky and wished tomorrow wouldn't come. *Retirement* was not a word I had ever prepared myself to hear.

The school board had graciously explained all the reasons they thought it was time for me to step back from teaching. My family had listened to me, reasoned with me, and prayed for me. It wasn't that I didn't understand. It was just that it hurt so much to say goodbye to something I lived for. The year was now 2002, marking thirty-one years in which teaching had been my life.

"But, Vera, you won't stop teaching. We all know you better than that. You'll find all sorts of ways to fill your hours with encouraging people and helping others. It will just be teaching in a different capacity." Johnny's kind words came back again and I smiled. I knew he was right. I wouldn't stop teaching. My life was full of friends and family and opportunities. And my health and stamina had been declining. It was getting harder and harder to cope physically and do my job well in the classroom.

But I would miss my students. And no matter how I told myself the truth, the facts didn't hurt any less. *God, help me accept this change with dignity. I've given everything I had to teach for you. Now help me to live for you outside the classroom the same way I lived in the classroom. You know it's my passion, God. But I'm trusting you to give me just as much purpose in this new season as you did for these wonderful thirty-one years of impacting lives through learning. God, you have been so good to me. So many wonderful memories . . ."*

My mind traveled back over the years, long ago to the first day of class when a scared young woman had entered that upper grade classroom and signed a high-sounding pledge before her first students. I smiled now at the thought. *How naïve and idealistic I was back then, but so hopeful and full of dreams and passion. Time teaches you in more ways than one. It mellows and softens and deepens . . .*

Outside, the leaves on the trees were in full glory of spring on the verge of summer. A robin trilled merrily, and I listened to his song through the open window. New life. My last class of students had been just that. Bursting with young life. They had been eager to learn and eager to love. Knowing it was my last year, I had savored every moment. Now tomorrow the final, formal sealing of my teaching career was to commence with a special service of appreciation.

The next morning I was extra particular about my appearance and dress. Lena graciously and patiently helped me until I was satisfied. I knew I would be seeing several hundred of my former students, and I wanted to honor them in return for their love for me. I had always taught them that careful attendance to dress, appearance, and manners expressed the godly quality of dignity and honor both to ourselves and to others.

"Remember when you used to teach us how to keep our nails trimmed and clean and manicured in girls' day at school?" my niece Emma chuckled.

"I certainly do," I smiled. "Oh! So many good memories."

"You'll be seeing some of your students that you haven't seen in years," Emma encouraged. "Are you excited?"

"Of course, it will be wonderful to see them. I still carry every one of them in my heart."

I felt a strange mixture of excitement and sorrow. The sorrow reminded me of the ache I felt when Mom had gone home to be with the Lord several years before, while the happiness of seeing and celebrating with everyone reminded me of the joy I felt in preparing a party for someone. It didn't make sense to feel such a strong mingling of both at once, and I prayed inwardly for strength to face the day.

When we arrived, I was greeted on every side by exclamations of love and warmth, along with firm handshakes, gentle hugs, and glowing smiles of remembrance and recognition. The packed auditorium buzzed around me. "Sister Vera! Remember that one Christmas program when I was a sheep?"

"Oh, yes! You made quite a frisky one," I recalled laughingly. "But it's been so long since I've seen you. How are you now?" I looked up into the face of a grown man who had once been a high-energy third grader in my classroom.

He chuckled. "Life has been pretty wooly since then, but all that you taught me has kept me following the Shepherd. He's been good, despite the ups and downs."

"I'm so glad to hear that. Nothing could make me happier than to know that my students are following Christ," I affirmed.

"Oh, and remember the monkey chains we'd make as we memorized our multiplication facts?" another student chimed in.

"Oh, yes! And the skating parties and sledding!"

As my former students flowed around me, memories washed over me in waves. It was so wonderful to be with my children like this, with so many of them in one place all at once.

When the program began, I watched each person get up to speak with a lump in my throat. *How often does one see so much love in one place?* I wondered. *Lord, I don't deserve this. All the honor goes to you. Thank you for allowing me to be a small part of your plan through these years.*

More than one original piece of poetry was shared in remembrance of my love of poetry and the years of teaching it. One written by my brother-in-law Johnny captured many of the lighter moments in my classroom. Since he couldn't be there that day, the poem was read by David Miller, the husband of my sister Judy.

"Oh, a life that is lived, when for others we give,
Isn't wasted or thrown far away;
But with love it is wrought, while with each lesson taught,
Will return as a crown some sweet day.

"Nearly four hundred strong, what an impressive throng,
As they marched through her class day by day,
And with soap she did teach against improper speech,
Much to many a big boy's dismay.

"We were taught to sit still waiting quiet on the hill,
Creative writing our sense to assail.
But with pet day a mess, though a major success,
Would cause lesser hearts often to fail.

"Winter picnics were fun, through the woods we would run,
With the golf cart along for the ride,
Though we nearly did freeze from the sharp, chilly breeze,
But we hid it because of our pride.

"Typing classes were had, though we sometimes were bad,
Yet we learned it in spite of our mess,
We kept pecking away until day after day,
We could keep up with all of the rest.

"Student profiles were made, and her Home Ec class stayed
Till we knew how to make each new dish.
Then they fixed it up right, and they served it at night
To their parents, and it was delish!

"Mathematics were hard, but with flashing the card,
Monkey chains from the ceiling were hung,
Till each multiplied fact, could be said with a snap,

And the monkeys placed back in their drum.

"There was Poem Day so good, that we'd come if we could
To hear poetry little and great,
We'd judge how they'd stand, and their movements of hand,
But the beauty of verse was first rate.

"Now to each of you here, come and draw very near,
For a secret I'm 'bout to disclose.
I don't think she will quit, not even one bit,
For she teaches wherever she goes."

Here my eyes clouded with unshed tears. I wouldn't quit. Every one of these lives was still mine to touch. Every heart here was still mine to love. With God's help I would continue to reach out and be a part of these lives that were so intermingled with my own. The final stanza reminded me of my purpose in life, and as David finished reading, his words echoed in my mind.

"Sister Vera, we say, and in many a way,
That we thank you for all that you've done,
And we'll tell you just now, there's a crown for your brow
Waiting you when your last battle's won!"

David looked out over the crowd, and his eyes briefly met mine with a brotherly smile. Clearing his throat, he spoke with feeling. "Sister Vera began her teaching career with a determination that was unstoppable. She was committed to doing her best, and today she stands head and shoulders above us as an example of good old-fashioned grit in the face of insurmountable obstacles; not to her students only, but to all of us who know and love her.

"Her indomitable spirit led her into paths of ingenious thought processes, and virgin stands of teaching techniques where she hewed out new ideas and put them to work in her classes and in the fertile minds of her students. To this day, her methods have taken root, and her growing ideas are bearing fruit in the lives of her students, a number of whom were challenged to also become teachers.

"Vera taught not only facts, information, and understanding, but she was never satisfied until she had reproduced the love of learning into the hearts of her students. They learned to love to read and to study out for themselves life's complex mysteries. Vera possesses that rare ability of leading students into mental exploration where God alone sets the boundaries. She led them "white-watering" through the uncharted canyons of struggle and on to the breath-taking peaks of success, and they have doggedly followed in her every footstep.

"As Vera's students become farmers, construction workers, pastors, teachers, fathers and mothers, they are better equipped for their journey through life for having been a student of Vera, for she taught them not only facts and how to apply them, but how to think, and how to live. She insisted on fairness and kind treatment of the under-achiever even while she motivated that struggling person to stretch just a little further, and try just a little harder. She demonstrated to many, through her own experience, how to knock the apostrophe and the 't' off of *can't,* and she introduced them to the taste of victory."

Here he paused again. I felt the lump that had been in my throat all morning swelling, and my chest felt heavy with emotion as he continued. "There exists a poem whose lines implore us to give our roses to the person we love and admire while they are yet living, rather than to lay them on their grave after they have departed. Vera, can you come up to the platform, please? Your students would like to present you with a special thank you."

On the platform, I watched from my wheelchair as various students of many ages came up one by one. Each of them offered me a beautiful rose of a different color. In all, there was a rose to represent each of the years I had taught. My eyes were full of tears as David looked at me and eloquently closed the tribute.

"Today, Vera, we offer you these roses. Savor them, preserve them, for they are given to you with all the love and appreciation you deserve; for your selfless sacrifice in making it possible for our children to learn, to love, and to live. But what are these when compared to the bouquet of glorified souls who will one day be gathered around that heavenly throne, many who have been assisted there by your hands?"

Suddenly it didn't matter so much that I was retiring. Eternity was what I was investing in. Each step of life could be correctly interpreted only in the light of Jesus' kingdom. We weren't living for time but for eternity. The gentle fragrance of the roses wafted up to me. Softly I fingered one of the velvety petals.

In retrospect, all the sorrow and change of life would seem like very little when I saw Him face to face. And today, in honor of that Love who had given so much for me and had led me so faithfully through every winding step of my life so far, I would choose to continue to live and give with all that I had, for *His* sake, until it was my turn to go home. *Lord, let me live every day with your sacrificial love. It truly will be worth it all when we see Christ*, I prayed silently as I bowed my head into the bouquet of love from the children God had given me.

A TRIBUTE
BY VICKY YODER

As one of the firsts in a bevy of nieces and nephews, my memories of Aunt Vera begin with the old farmhouse on Knox School Road.

She celebrated each of us as we came into the world. We were cradled in the crook of her arm as she lay on the sofa. As we grew, she gave us "pony rides" and thumped our bottoms with her feet. We grew up feeling we were the smartest, strongest, and most beautiful children ever born.

The old farmstead was the hub of our lives: we cousins all lived nearby and found every chance to gather for games of softball, football, ice-skating on the pond, or sledding on the hills out back. Vera was often nearby, watching from the sidelines, perched at a picnic table with her ever-present glass of iced tea, or from the front seat of a warm car. She would yell instructions and cheer with all her might, and if our ice-skating prowess was exceptional, would reach across to the steering wheel and honk the horn . . . with her toes! We knew she was watching us: we could feel it. Under her gaze, we became star athletes, Olympians—champions all the way!

School days were punctuated by her "yearly events," as she called them. Vera started school every September with a bang, and even the most reluctant students exchanged the carefree days of summer with a willing heart because they knew that learning with Vera was an adventure, and they couldn't wait for the journey to begin.

Supper at her house (cooked by and for the students) got the new school year off to a great start. With Vera's tiny fingers directing us, we sang our hearts out at the local nursing home, which gave us a valuable warm-up for the "real" program several weeks later. We wrote poetry on windy hilltops and knew we were the next budding Frosts or Longfellows. We gathered papery autumn leaves and pressed them in dusty old dictionaries to turn into art projects, and peered through a microscope lens at living brine shrimp and—*gasp!*—a drop of blood. Our little plastic monkeys clawed their way to the top of a monkey chain, advancing with every multiplication table learned. These events were steps in the long journey of learning, and with Vera, it was an adventure.

Our young adult years found us promoted to the honor of Travel Companion, Schoolroom Aide, or Shopping-and-Out-to-Eat Valet. Although Molly the Standing Wheelchair required some assembly for these outings, we knew we were more than bag-carriers and door-openers: Vera needed our help, but she also valued and enjoyed our company.

World Book Encyclopedia dealers' meetings, local and national post-polio conferences, and Joni and Friends Family Retreats provided a rich kaleidoscope of people and experiences. As a guest speaker at ladies' groups, churches, and children's ministries, Vera demonstrated her "Molly" and instructed her audience on the finer points of relating to handicapped people. We loved going along to these events, and Vera never failed to introduce us as her biggest support group: her family.

Retirement after teaching for so many years was definitely a time of transition for Vera. Instead of a classroom full of children, she tutored older children who needed an academic boost. To her great pleasure, one young man learned to read, which became a life-changing accomplishment for him. One-on-one, one at a time, lives were impacted for good, right at the dining room table, with Vera seated nearby. The formula was simple: instruction, a challenge to do and be the very best, and loads of encouragement. It worked!

Every afternoon was "'happy hour." From 3:00 to 4:00 we all knew the coffee was perking, and Vera would love to visit with anyone who had a chance to stop in. Aunts, cousins, and friends met to talk, plan, laugh, and dream over the events of their lives. Summer afternoons found us on the porch sipping iced tea, with neighbors honking a friendly hello as they passed. We solved the world's problems and a few of our own as conversation and love flowed around us.

After years of wrestling with Mollies One and Two, Vera was finally convinced that a mobilized wheelchair would improve her mobility when leaving the house. Like a queen on a throne, she rolled into restaurants, churches, or shopping malls, while we, the loyal subjects, scurried ahead to clear the way. The chair was always equipped for any emergency and any change in temperature: tote bags with blankets, water bottles, pillows, and even a miniature fan! She could maneuver the chair with a flick of her tiny fingers. What a sense of accomplishment it gave her.

Unlike her faithful standing chairs, the new and improved version did not fit into the trunk of a car. Through generous donations, a wheelchair-accessible van was purchased. Although she couldn't drive the new set of wheels herself, her position from the front passenger area gave her the unquestioned rank as chief navigator, flight engineer, and security manager all in one. The van was wonderful: it even gathered the five sisters and took them on road trips together!

Vera and her faithful friend, Bruce Fry, collaborated to form a mini-ministry called "God Is Love" and strategized to bring love and laughter to people in need throughout the surrounding communities. Birthday parties, hospital visits to the sick, and dinners were all part of their routine. Bruce's house in Carrollton became the home base for these occasions. Vera planned the menus and entertained the guests while Bruce cooked and hosted, all the while cheering on and encouraging as they served. Although Vera is no longer serving with this ministry, her van, willed to Bruce, helps to transport those in need of a lift, whether they are in a wheelchair or not.

The last six months of Vera's life saw big changes in her physical strength. A stroke weakened her lungs, and her BiPAP machine was needed for longer periods of time. Much of her daytime hours were spent on a daybed in the dining room, where she was still close to the action but able to be comfortable. On February 22, 2012, after suffering another mini-stroke, Vera quietly passed away at the age of sixty-three.

We gathered to grieve, cry, laugh, and remember our teacher, friend, aunt, and sister. Each of us had been touched by Vera, especially by her encouragement to carry on even though the carrying was tough. The mourners included people from many walks of life: pastors, teachers, businessmen, fathers and mothers, the elderly, the very young, the gifted, those who have struggled, and those who live with challenges. A common true thread bound us all together: this tiny, frail dynamo of a teacher/mentor had, through unfailing faith and love for each of us, cheered us on to be all that we could be. It was now our turn.

In our hearts we all told her, "Run fast, our little champion! Fly over those streets of gold and claim your prize. You struggled against the odds and . . . you won!"

ABOUT THE AUTHOR

Rachael originates from the lovely Northwoods of Minnesota, but these days you'll rarely find her there. Whether it's research for another writing project, opportunities to serve in a refugee camp in Greece, or teaching English in India, she is always eager to pack her bags.

When she's not writing, she enjoys other passions such as spending time with her nieces and nephews, building meaningful friendships, reading deep books, trying new coffee drink recipes, and learning more about the peoples and cultures of the Middle East. Rachael is blessed to share in the lives of those she writes about.

Her passion for writing remains alive as God opens new doors of opportunity. "To be a scribe recording just one small chapter of His story as He works among His children is a huge privilege," she says. "When I write, I feel His pleasure, and it's my heart's desire that what flows from my pen would be for His glory alone."

Rachael enjoys hearing from her readers and invites you to email her at ascribebytrade@gmail.com. You may also write to her in care of Christian Aid Ministries, P.O. Box 360, Berlin, Ohio, 44610.

CHRISTIAN AID MINISTRIES

Christian Aid Ministries was founded in 1981 as a nonprofit, tax-exempt 501(c)(3) organization. Its primary purpose is to provide a trustworthy and efficient channel for Amish, Mennonite, and other conservative Anabaptist groups and individuals to minister to physical and spiritual needs around the world. This is in response to the command to ". . . do good unto all men, especially unto them who are of the household of faith" (Galatians 6:10).

Each year, CAM supporters provide approximately 15 million pounds of food, clothing, medicines, seeds, Bibles, Bible story books, and other Christian literature for needy people. Most of the aid goes to orphans and Christian families. Supporters' funds also help to clean up and rebuild for natural disaster victims, put up Gospel billboards in the U.S., support several church-planting efforts, operate two medical clinics, and provide resources for needy families to make their own living. CAM's main purposes for providing aid are to help and encourage God's people and bring the Gospel to a lost and dying world.

CAM has staff, warehouses, and distribution networks in Romania,

Moldova, Ukraine, Haiti, Nicaragua, Liberia, and Israel. Aside from management, supervisory personnel, and bookkeeping operations, volunteers do most of the work at CAM locations. Each year, volunteers at our warehouses, field bases, Disaster Response Services projects, and other locations donate over 200,000 hours of work.

CAM's ultimate purpose is to glorify God and help enlarge His kingdom. ". . . whatsoever ye do, do all to the glory of God" (1 Corinthians 10:31).

THE WAY TO GOD AND PEACE

We live in a world contaminated by sin. Sin is anything that goes against God's holy standards. When we do not follow the guidelines that God our Creator gave us, we are guilty of sin. Sin separates us from God, the source of life.

Since the time when the first man and woman, Adam and Eve, sinned in the Garden of Eden, sin has been universal. The Bible says that we all have "sinned and come short of the glory of God" (Romans 3:23). It also says that the natural consequence for that sin is eternal death, or punishment in an eternal hell: "Then when lust hath conceived, it bringeth forth sin: and sin, when it is finished, bringeth forth death" (James 1:15).

But we do not have to suffer eternal death in hell. God provided forgiveness for our sins through the death of His only Son, Jesus Christ. Because Jesus was perfect and without sin, He could die in our place. "For God so loved the world that he gave his only begotten Son, that whosoever believeth in him should not perish, but have everlasting life" (John 3:16).

A sacrifice is something given to benefit someone else. It costs the giver greatly. Jesus was God's sacrifice. Jesus' death takes away the penalty of sin for everyone who accepts this sacrifice and truly repents of their sins. To repent of sins means to be truly sorry for and turn away from the things we have done that have violated God's standards (Acts 2:38; 3:19).

Jesus died, but He did not remain dead. After three days, God's Spirit miraculously raised Him to life again. God's Spirit does something similar in us. When we receive Jesus as our sacrifice and repent of our sins, our hearts are changed. We become spiritually alive! We develop new desires and attitudes (2 Corinthians 5:17). We begin to make choices that please God (1 John 3:9). If we do fail and commit sins, we can ask God for forgiveness. "If we confess our sins, he is faithful and just to forgive us our sins, and to cleanse us from all unrighteousness" (1 John 1:9).

Once our hearts have been changed, we want to continue growing spiritually. We will be happy to let Jesus be the Master of our lives and will want to become more like Him. To do this, we must meditate on God's Word and commune with God in prayer. We will testify to others of this change by being baptized and sharing the good news of God's victory over sin and death. Fellowship with a faithful group of believers will strengthen our walk with God (1 John 1:7).